Community Surveys with Local Talent:

A Handbook

NORC Report No. 123

By
EVE WEINBERG

NATIONAL OPINION RESEARCH CENTER
The University of Chicago

This document was prepared on behalf of the Program Planning and Evaluation Division of the Office of Health Affairs, Office of Economic Opportunity.

Published by
National Opinion Research Center
6030 South Ellis Avenue
Chicago, Illinois 60637

Library of Congress Catalog Card Number 77-148016

Printed in the United States of America

ACKNOWLEDGMENTS

Three health centers--Charles R. Drew Neighborhood Health Center, Red Hook Neighborhood Health Center, and the Atlanta Southside Comprehensive Health Center--were the pioneers in this project. The staff and boards of these health centers deserve first mention among the many who, directly or indirectly, have been helpful in the preparation of this handbook.

Gerald Sparer, Director of the Program Planning and Evaluation Division of the Office of Health Affairs of OEO, has been a staunch supporter of the project from the beginning. In fact, it was he who conceived the idea that a "how-to-do-it" handbook should be one of the products of NORC's experience. We appreciate the freedom and encouragement that he has given us at NORC to develop the handbook as we saw fit. He read several drafts of the manuscript and made a number of insightful suggestions, but the ideas expressed herein, whether good or bad, are our own.

At NORC I am grateful to Norman M. Bradburn, Director of NORC, whose faith in me has been a constant source of encouragement, and to Paul B. Sheatsley, under whose overall guidance all the health center surveys have been conducted. William C. Richardson, who was responsible for the direction of the first three surveys, provided me with helpful criticisms and suggestions, particularly in the early phases of the work.

Pearl Zinner, NORC's eastern field director, and Roslyn Weisinger and Lucille Kolkin, senior field supervisors of NORC's New York staff, reviewed several drafts carefully and made important suggestions, most of which were incorporated. Their suggestions were particularly meaningful since Mrs. Weisinger and

Mrs. Kolkin were in charge of the supervision of the Bedford-Crown Heights (Charles R. Drew Neighborhood Health Center) and Red Hook surveys, respectively. Each of them was responsible for the many reports and running records of those two surveys, upon which I have relied heavily in the preparation of this handbook.

Special thanks go to Fansayde Calloway, supervisor of the Atlanta survey and assistant field director of NORC. Fan Calloway, more than any other person, helped me to see that not only is there an enormous resource of talent in urban communities, but that when properly motivated and trained, this "resource of talent"--just people in the community--can be mobilized to work profitably for themselves and advantageously for their communities.

Thanks also go to Carol Stocking and Miriam Clarke, who each read and commented on a draft of the manuscript. Harriet Adams cheerfully typed and retyped many drafts of the manuscript and, with the help of Annot Littleton, proofread them all. NORC's editor, Mary Spaeth, helped me sharpen my ideas and clarify the language of the text. Her assistant, Elaine Richardson, performed yeoman service in the preparation of the appendices. The final manuscript of the text was typed by NORC's steno pool with most of the typing being done by Nancy Nagel and Mary Okazaki. The cover photograph was taken by Frances Harris.

All these people helped to make the handbook a more useful document. The deficiencies that remain are my own responsibility.

Last, but not least, my family--my husband, Norman, and Judy, Ellen, Michael, and Robert--all gave up many hours of their own time to help out with cooking meals or doing the marketing, while their wife and mother was at work on this handbook. To all of the above, my sincere thanks.

E.W.

TABLE OF CONTENTS

TABLE OF CONTENTS--Continued

TABLE OF CONTENTS--Continued

TABLE OF CONTENTS--Continued

LIST OF TABLES

INTRODUCTION

Under a master agreement with the Office of Economic Opportunity, the National Opinion Research Center (NORC) carried out base-line health surveys of the population in a number of health center target areas throughout the United States during 1968 and 1969. The major purposes of the surveys were to establish base-line data on the extent and patterns of health care and to gather demographic and various other kinds of data about community residents in order to aid the newly established neighborhood health centers in the planning and evaluation of health services.

Some of the target areas were more heterogeneous in population than others, but all of them contained a high proportion of poor people. NORC's agreement included, therefore, the stipulation that the interviewers for the surveys be selected from residents within the target area, and that some preference be given to people who were either unemployed or underemployed. A further condition of the agreement was that the interviewers would be employees of the health centers, even though they would be selected, trained, and supervised by NORC field supervisors.

Prior to undertaking this project, NORC's experience in training the poor to interview the poor had been limited. We came to realize that our task on these surveys constituted not a <u>difference in degree</u> from the standard NORC hiring and training procedures (geared to middle-class interviewers), but a <u>difference in kind</u>. This realization allowed us to plan and staff the health surveys in a totally different way. We established close working relations with the health center staffs, the community boards, and the advisory councils. In other words, we were there to assist the local community and the local professionals in whatever way necessary to achieve a valid and reliable base-line survey of the health care and behavior of the residents in the target area, and to do this while providing jobs to people in the community.

The data collected by the interviewers on the health center surveys are comparable in accuracy and quality to those collected by the "typical" middle-class survey research interviewer. The difference is that people with less education and less experience in working with written materials require more initial training, more continuous training, and more and closer supervision in order to collect the same quality of information as middle-class interviewers. Where funds are available, we feel it is well worth the investment for the extra training and supervision costs.

The purpose of this handbook is to set forth guidelines for conducting the field interviewing portion of a sample survey in a low-income area. This volume does not contain any information about survey design, questionnaire design, coding and processing of data, or analysis. Those activities were all carried out at NORC and the results are presented in various individual reports to the Office of Health Affairs of the Office of Economic Opportunity. This document does include information about all activities carried out by NORC personnel in the target areas. It is primarily based on NORC's experiences in the Bedford-Crown Heights and Red Hook areas of Brooklyn, New York, and in the Southwest area of Atlanta, Georgia--the first three target areas in which NORC undertook health center surveys. It reflects as well some experiences gained from health center surveys conducted in Philadelphia, Pennsylvania; Washington, D.C.; Charleston, South Carolina; East Palo Alto, California; and San

Francisco, California. Experiences reported here are based entirely on strict area probability sampling and on sample sizes designed to yield interviews with either 1,000 or 1,500 households, depending on the population size of the target area. The initial goal required hiring from thirty to sixty interviewers, again depending on the specific community.

This handbook is addressed specifically to communities interested in replicating NORC's methods of selecting, training, and supervising local residents as interviewers in health survey target areas. Large portions of it, however, would be useful to researchers wishing to conduct any kind of survey in areas such as OEO target areas. The section on orientation meetings and portions of the chapter on training should be useful to anyone interested in training groups of interviewers or, for that matter, training any previously unemployed or underemployed persons to become useful employees in a variety of occupations. Learning about "how to meet the public," proper dress, punctuality, increased vocabulary, and pride in one's accomplishments have applications in many occupations besides interviewing. We feel that in training people to be interviewers, we are able at the same time to give them a basic understanding of good work habits and pride in their own portion of the work. With the proper follow-through, such interviewers can become active participants in the labor force.

CHAPTER I

PRELIMINARY ARRANGEMENTS

The first step in beginning a field-interviewing survey in a target area is to establish working relations with the community in which the survey is to be conducted. Too often survey organizations initiate the field interviewing with little explanation to either community residents or community leaders. In recent years, local leaders in many communities have become wary of "outsiders" who come in to conduct surveys. NORC's experience indicates that when leaders of the community are consulted and apprised of the legitimate intent, purpose, and use of a community survey, they tend to be interested and helpful in accomplishing the task. The better the relationship between the surveyor and community leaders, the greater the cooperation that the interviewers receive from community residents.

In the special case of a neighborhood health center survey, the definition of "community" is usually clear--it is the target area established by the boundaries set for the health center. What is perhaps less clear is who all the community representatives are with whom one should establish rapport. We do know that they include such persons as the elected members of the community board of the health center. The community board is usually the governing body that makes the decision to have the survey. Some neighborhood health centers find it helpful, in addition, to appoint a health advisory council composed of representatives from the board and the medical staff and of individuals from the community. A health advisory council may be appointed permanently or just for the purpose of working on some specific problem or task. The staff of the health center, while not technically representing the community, do work in the community and are often heavily involved in community liaison work. Thus, members of the community board, of the advisory council (if there is one), and of the health center staff are the obvious people to work with first in establishing the survey organization in the community.

Once the center has made the decision to have a survey, a number of preliminary arrangements need to be worked out in order to get the survey operation off to a good start. A great deal depends on how well the representatives of the funding agency and of the survey organization present the value of a baseline survey. The survey field supervisor usually appears on the scene several weeks after preliminary conversations have begun and at a time when some of the arrangements have already been made.

Relations between the Health Center Board, Staff, and Survey Supervisor

One of the first tasks of the survey field supervisor is to meet the staff of the health center. Sometimes the administrator or some other liaison person on the staff initiates this meeting, and sometimes the survey supervisor initiates it. The meeting can occur in a group at a staff meeting, or it can be on an individual basis, with the supervisor talking with each staff person about his or her particular interest and possible connection with the survey. The staff members who tend to be most involved with various aspects of the health survey are the community organizer, the training director, someone from the payroll department, and the medical director. Since the personalities of those holding such positions vary, our survey supervisor has had to work out specific relationships with appropriate staff members. In each center this has represented a unique grouping of specific staff positions.

Usually after the supervisor has met the staff, she[1] may be asked to attend a meeting of the community board and/or health advisory council. The survey may be either the main reason for the meeting or one of many items on the agenda. In either case, the survey supervisor will be expected to discuss briefly the kind of survey to be conducted, its purpose, and perhaps the kind of sample to be used. Primarily, however, she is there to acquaint the elected representatives of the community with the number of temporary jobs that the survey will provide for persons in the community. This meeting offers a good opportunity for the supervisor to discuss what she knows from past experience about the kind of person who is best suited for interviewing: someone who has native intelligence (not necessarily a high school graduate), can read and write well enough to handle the questionnaire and written instructions, is interested in people and curious about them, is physically healthy enough to climb stairs when necessary, does not mind knocking on doors without a prior introduction, is prepared to work some evenings and/or weekends in case some people in the assignment are not available for interviews during the day, and is generally interested in a job that provides training not only for additional interviewing but for many other jobs that involve meeting the public and carrying out a number of clerical tasks.

The survey supervisor should tell the health center community board and/or health advisory council what guidelines will be used in the selection of interviewers. While, in every case, the contract between NORC and the health center stipulated the requirement that local residents be hired to perform the various survey tasks, we found in most cases that the board needed to be

---

[1]The word "she" is used when referring to the survey supervisor since most of NORC's supervisors are women. There is, of course, no a priori reason why the supervisor could not be a man.

reassured that these standards would be upheld. The meeting with the board is a good time to stress that first preference in hiring will be given to persons who are unemployed and second preference to persons who are underemployed. The Memo to Interviewer Applicants, which is described later in this chapter and presented in Appendix A, should be made available to board members. If pay rates for the survey have not yet been determined, this meeting may be the one at which the suggested pay rate is discussed and hopefully brought to a vote. The survey supervisor can be helpful as a resource person in such a discussion.[2]

In summary, at the meeting with the board or council, the survey field supervisor should be able to answer any questions, clear up any misinformation, and possibly distribute some written materials so that no misconceptions arise about the survey, who will be interviewed, who the interviewers will be, how many interviewers will be hired, how many applicants the supervisor feels should apply (from which those with the highest chance for success as interviewers will be selected), how much the interviewers will be paid, and how long these temporary jobs will be likely to last.

Housing for the Survey Office

Survey office space should be found as soon as the survey field supervisor arrives. Ideally this office should be within the health center, but most centers are short of space themselves. Therefore, it is usually necessary to search for space nearby to accommodate the survey office. Such an arrangement is entirely adequate.

---

[2]A note of caution: If this is a large, open community meeting, it would be unwise to attempt a discussion of pay rates. An authorized committee should be consulted in that case.

Our experience indicates that the survey office needs one large room for the training sessions and meetings with all the interviewers, plus one or more smaller rooms for the supervisor, secretary, editors, and clerical staff. There must be adequate toilet facilities, a water cooler, and regular maintenance. Housing must have a dignified and pleasant appearance, whether it is in the health center or nearby.

During the initial period of several weeks, the larger room is in full-time use for the interviewer recruiting and training sessions. After that, some space must be provided to seat comfortably the clerical and editorial personnel. (The large room used for training could be used for that purpose if not needed by the health center for other purposes.) It is desirable to have at least one additional private office (or arrangement of furniture so there is some privacy) where the supervisor can conduct conversations with interviewers on a one-to-one basis. A number of items of furniture and supplies are necessary for a smooth functioning operation. These are listed in Appendix B. The survey office should be furnished and properly equipped before the recruitment of interviewers begins.

Payment Policies for Interviewers

Before anyone in the community is alerted to the availability of jobs, the pay rates for these jobs must be established by the health center board. The survey supervisor must know the starting rate as well as any increments that may be available after successful completion of various tasks. The supervisor must also know when the pay periods will be. In our experience, it is best to devise a one- or two-page memorandum describing the interviewer's job, which can be distributed to all persons interested in the job. This memorandum should contain the pay rate.

NORC has designed a standard time sheet for interviewers working on health center studies. This sheet should be approved by the health center's payroll department, which will be handling the payment of interviewer wages since the interviewers are employees of the health center. (A revised copy of the Interviewer's Time Report can be found in Appendix B.)

Hiring Other Survey Personnel

Clerks

From among those persons applying for interviewer jobs, there are usually some with particular aptitudes for clerical tasks who can be spotted early in the training period. At the end of the training, about two such persons should be assigned as field office assistants to handle the clerical tasks of checking in the interviews and otherwise assisting with the office work.

Secretary

The health center should hire one secretary who is assigned to the survey office from the very beginning until the completion of the survey. This person should be someone whom the center could later incorporate into its own staff. Making sure that such a person is available about the time the survey supervisor wants to begin work is clearly part of the preliminary arrangements. The secretary should ideally be somewhat familiar with office procedures and should be able to type neatly. (Speed in typing is helpful but not necessary.) She should be able to work full time. It is particularly helpful if the secretary is adept at working with simple figures since she is the ideal person to be the "timekeeper" for the survey office, i.e., to check the interviewers' time sheets for accuracy and to total the various columns. She should have a pleasant, friendly personality since she has contact with interviewers and respondents on the phone and in person.

Editors

The editors' jobs are more difficult to fill since they require considerable experience with questionnaires and other written material. Editors check the quality of the completed interviews. They look for errors, omissions, and inconsistencies, and they discuss with the individual interviewers problems that appear in their work. We have found that experienced interviewers are particularly good at this task, but few of them live in the target area.

Interviewer Materials

Identification Cards

A facsimile of NORC's standard ID card is presented in Appendix B along with a facsimile of an ID card developed for a health survey. While it is not necessary to work out the details of the ID card in the preliminary stages, it is a good idea to alert the health center liaison person to the need for ID cards.

Carrying Cases

The materials that the interviewers carry with them in the field are voluminous, and we have found it necessary to provide some sort of carrying case to hold these materials. Inexpensive plastic briefcases are available in most cities and are well worth the cost. New interviewers enjoy the professional image that carrying a briefcase implies. A good time to request authorization for the purchase of carrying cases is during the preliminary arrangement stage.

Letters to Respondents

In some areas it is appropriate to mail a letter to each household that falls into the sample in order to alert the residents to the interviewer's call, to tell them a bit about the study, and to urge their cooperation. In other areas it is best to prepare such a letter but have the interviewer hand it to the residents rather than mail it (see Appendix D for a sample letter). The content of the letter can be suggested by the survey organization but should be approved by representatives of the community and reproduced on health center stationery.

Leaflet Describing Health Center

One can assume that many residents of the target area will be either unaware of the existence of the health center (if indeed it does exist at the time of the survey) or unclear about what it does and whom it serves. It is wise to develop a small leaflet describing the health center, what it does (or will do), whom it serves, and how the residents can find out more about it. The interviewers can be given a supply of these leaflets to leave with respondents after the interview. Obviously, the content must be developed by the staff of the center.

CHAPTER II

THE SELECTION OF INTERVIEWERS

Recruitment of Interviewer Applicants

The recruitment process, probably more than any other phase of the field work, varies from community to community. The composition and interest of the health center board, the extent of involvement of the health center staff, and the roles each may wish to play in the recruiting process are important factors that affect how and by whom the recruiting of interviewers is carried out. In addition, a great deal depends simply on the "mood" of the community at the time.

Roles in the Recruitment Process

As might be guessed, there are three prime movers in the recruitment process--the health center board, the health center staff, and the survey supervisor. Keeping in mind local contingencies, we state here what we recommend as the most desirable division of labor and responsibility to accomplish the task of recruitment effectively and efficiently.

The health center board members.--Board members are in the best position to publicize the recruiting program among their friends, relatives, and neighbors in the community. Their role should be one of providing community residents with correct information about the survey jobs, not one of making promises about jobs. Board members should feel free to call the survey field supervisor with names for consideration as long as the persons referred reside in the target area.

The health center staff.--The ideal situation is one in which one particular staff member is assigned to familiarize the survey supervisor with applications of local residents for various, previously publicized jobs. Names in the health center office files of local persons interested in working at the center are also useful. At this stage, any name with an address in the target area is better than no name. These names and addresses should be supplied to the survey field supervisor. In addition, there may already be an Outreach Program in the community, in which case its training director can be useful by making the recruiting process known through his Outreach trainees or workers. If there is a community organizer on the health center staff, that person should be helpful in mentioning the survey in the community and in helping recruit interviewer applicants.

The survey field supervisor.--The survey supervisor has the responsibility to follow up on every name she is given. The procedure we have followed requires that a letter and memo (See Appendix A) be sent to all persons whose names have been given to the supervisor (provided they live in the target area). In the letter they are asked to read the memo and then call for an appointment if they are interested in applying. Each person who calls is given a choice of days and times to attend one of the scheduled orientation meetings, where further details about the interviewing job will be discussed. Selections for the interviewing jobs are made from among those who come to the orientation meetings and follow through on the next steps.

Other role combinations.--Obviously, there are a number of other possible combinations of roles to accomplish the recruitment of interviewers. Included in these is what amounts to almost the opposite procedure from that discussed above. On one of our studies, the survey field supervisor and her staff did all of the recruiting by means of publicity in newspapers, contact with local PTAs and other community groups, word-of-mouth, a radio spot, etc. After the orientation meeting had been held and the applicants had completed the initial step of conducting two try-out interviews, the supervisor made recommendations on hiring to a selected representative of the health center board, who checked on whether the applicants fulfilled the residency requirement before they were hired. The supervisor did not submit the name of any applicant for whom she felt success in interviewing was very unlikely. As it turned out, those recruited in this fashion were all approved by the board.

Although the health center is hiring and paying the interviewers, the survey field supervisor is responsible for the training of the interviewers and for the quality of the interviews once the field work begins. One would assume that board members would not submit names of anyone whom they would not wish hired, nor would the health center files contain names of persons unacceptable to the center. Further, it would seem that board members and staff members would be in a much better position to recruit from the community than would the survey supervisor who, in most cases, will be new in the community. Therefore, for the recruiting process we recommend a division of labor and responsibility whereby the board members and staff of the health center supply the survey supervisor with all possible recruits from the target area and then the survey supervisor uses her best professional judgment in selecting from among them those persons who have the highest probability of success as interviewers. However, if sufficient applicants are not forthcoming, or if the health center staff or board do not have the time or know-how, the survey supervisor will have to take a more active role in recruiting applicants.

Orientation Meetings

The orientation meetings, conducted by the survey field supervisor or a trainer who works with her, are group sessions at which prospective interviewer applicants are informed in some detail about the job for which they may be applying. Orientation sessions should be scheduled for both daytime and evening hours to allow maximum attendance by interested persons. It is best to keep the size of each meeting to no larger than twelve or thirteen people, so that those in attendance will be free to participate and ask questions and will not be intimidated by the sheer number of other applicants.

The number of such meetings depends on the total number of interviewers required for the survey. If the sample size is about 2,000 households--enough to yield 1,500 completed interviews when the vacant units and nonrespondents are taken into account--it is best to begin the field work with approximately fifty to fifty-five interviewers. Since we know that the attrition rate between those who attend orientation meetings and those who are invited to training is considerable, we recommend inviting from three to five times as many persons to the orientation sessions (depending on the particular area) as will eventually be hired. In Brooklyn, NORC actually saw almost five times as many people at orientation meetings as were eventually hired, while in Atlanta the number was closer to three times as many.

Orientation meetings provide a side benefit by furnishing an excellent opportunity to invite interested board members or staff members to observe the process of interviewer applicants being oriented to the job. The response that this type of orientation can elicit from the applicant will be of interest to board or staff members.

A typical orientation meeting would include discussion of the following matters:

Nature and purpose of the health survey and how it relates to the health center

Role of the interviewer on the health survey

Job of interviewing and its requirements

Rate of pay and payment policies

Interviewing techniques, including a review of the written interviewer instructions that are part of the try-out kit (see sample of try-out kit materials in Appendix A) and that the applicant will be expected to study. Suggestions are given on how to study and prepare for the try-out interviews, and mock interviews are conducted.

Scheduling of each applicant's second appointment, when the completed try-out interviews will be constructively reviewed by the supervisor.

Completion of application form (see sample in Appendix A)

To illustrate in more human terms what happens in an orientation meeting, we quote from the report of one of the supervisors:

> Each applicant had been provided with a memo describing the job and its qualifications. They were seated around large conference tables with the trainer and materials at the cross-table. They were told that prior to their making formal application, we would discuss some things about the job and its requirements so that they could decide whether this was of interest to them. After introduction and some background information, the trainer put the following phrases on the blackboard:
>
> (a) 21 years of age or older
> (b) ability to read with understanding
> (c) write clearly
> (d) relate well with people
> (e) physically able to visit the assigned home
>
> The group was invited to give their opinions as to why each of these criteria would be important for an interviewer on the health study. By enlisting their participation in this way, they were able to grasp the importance of their role and I was able to observe their alertness and ability to articulate. There was never any problem in getting them to respond readily to these phrases. Each opinion was written down on a second blackboard and discussed further by them or me.

When the time came to introduce the try-out questionnaire and specifications, it was explained that since I wanted all to perform at their highest level, so that selection would be most difficult for me to make, I would review the contents of the specifications (i.e., interviewer instructions) and go over most of the questionnaire in mock interview. The mock interview was done by alternately using applicants or the trainer as the respondent. Important techniques described in the specifications were pointed out and emphasized as the interview proceeded. Certain key words which are basic to an interviewer's vocabulary were explained and written on the blackboard. All open-ended questions were recorded on the board with probe marks to impress their usage.

At the end of the session, which usually lasted about one and a half hours, applicants were invited to complete their application form and take a try-out kit. Individual appointments were set up for the return of the materials about three days later.

Try-Out Interviews

Try-out interviews may be used by the supervisor as a screening device. Those applicants who return for their second appointment have given evidence that they are really interested in working, and no matter how bad the try-out interviews are, chances are very good that the applicant is trainable and should enter the interviewer training program. NORC's try-out interviews (see Appendix A) are designed to give applicants an opportunity to be exposed to the types of questions that they will encounter on the actual survey and to experience the interviewing situation itself. Applicants are told that at least one of the two people they select to interview on the try-out questionnaire should be a stranger. The other may be a member of their family or a friend. The try-out interviews are therefore also a sort of screening device for the applicants. The applicant who feels uncomfortable in a stranger's home is less likely to want to go through with the application for interviewing.

The unanswered question is: How many of the applicants who do not return with completed try-out questionnaires would also have made good interviewers? Is it perhaps that some applicants view the try-out questionnaire as yet another "test" to see whether or not they measure up to a standard that someone else has set, and therefore they do not return for fear of being rejected?

In the Bedford-Crown area of Brooklyn and in Atlanta, we used the try-out interviews as described. In the Red Hook area of Brooklyn, at the request of health center staff members and after initial response was below expectations, we invited everyone who attended the orientation meetings to become a trainee without conducting the try-out interviews. Table II.1 shows the flow of applicants from orientation meetings to try-out questionnaires and/or training in the three areas.

Several things are clear in looking at the comparative data in the table. First, the return rate (with completed try-out questionnaires) in Red Hook prior to September 17 not only was not poor, but was actually better, in percentage terms, than in either Atlanta or Bedford-Crown. Second, the try-out questionnaires do seem to serve the function of allowing people to select themselves out if they find that interviewing is not what they had envisioned. The table points up the fact that while approximately one-fourth of the people who attended orientation meetings in Atlanta and Bedford-Crown actually received an interviewing assignment, only one-fifth of them got to that point in Red Hook when the try-out interviews were not used as an additional screening or self-selection device. One could argue that perhaps Red Hook was "different," and the attrition rate was bound to be higher. However, when try-out interviews were used in the earlier recruiting period in Red Hook, the attrition rate was in fact the lowest.

TABLE II.1

ATTRITION OF APPLICANTS DURING SELECTION PROCESS IN THREE AREAS IN 1968

Steps in Selection Process	Atlanta (Apr. 18 to May 15)	Bedford-Crown (Apr. 12 to May 27)	Red Hook[a]		
			(Aug. 7 to Sept. 17)	(Sept. 17 to Oct. 4)	Total
Attended orientation meeting	110	236	68	164	232
Eliminated self (did not keep appointment for personal interview)	30	128	24	106	130
Eliminated by trainer (not qualified)	20	16	-	-	-
Received personal interview and completed 2 try-out questionnaires	60 (55%)	92 (39%)	44 (65%)	-	102 (44%)
Eliminated by trainer (not qualified or did not return after second chance to qualify)	12	-	17	-	17
Qualified, but not invited to training (staff already large enough) . . .	18	5	-	-	-
Invited to training	30 (27%)	87 (37%)	27 (40%)	58 (35%)	85 (37%)
Eliminated self (never came to training)	-	24	-	-	-
Eliminated self (left training before completion	-	7	4	9	13
Eliminated self (completed training but left before interviewing began) . . .	2	-	4	12	16
Eliminated by trainer (not qualified after training)	-	-	-	4	4
Began interviewing	28 (25%)	56 (24%)	19 (28%)	33 (20%)	52 (22%)

[a] The recruiting process in Red Hook from August 7 to September 17 was identical to that in Atlanta and Bedford-Crown. At the suggestion of the health center staff, after September 17 applicants were invited into training sessions immediately after they attended an orientation meeting, without doing any try-out interviews. Thus, all of the 164 persons who attended orientation meetings in this period were invited to training, but 106 of them chose not to apply, leaving 58 who started training.

We conclude that the experiment of eliminating the try-out interviews as a screening device was well worth trying, but we believe the matter can now be laid to rest, with one caution. It must be made clear to all persons attending the orientation meetings that the purpose of the try-out interviews is as much to give the applicant a chance to "try out interviewing" as it is an opportunity for the supervisor to learn something about the person's aptitude for the job. We would strongly recommend the use of some sort of try-out interview as part of the application process.

Personal Interviews with Interviewer Applicants

As mentioned earlier, appointments for personal interviews with the applicants usually occur approximately three days after the orientation meeting. This is when the survey supervisor needs some additional assistance from other trainers. Sometimes the people who have been hired to do the field editing of questionnaires are available at this time, and they are most useful. Scheduling can become difficult at this particular period since orientation meetings are still being held for some applicants while others are returning for their individual appointments.

It is particularly important at this time to have available some office space with privacy so that each individual interview with an applicant can be conducted in privacy and each applicant can receive the necessary amount of time and attention. In some instances, when the applicants have made a considerable number of errors on their try-out interviews, they have volunteered to conduct another interview, or the trainer has requested an additional one after discussing the problems and offering suggestions. Rarely has an applicant not been given a second chance to try out. Applicants are told at the end of the interview that they will be notified about whether they have been accepted or rejected as soon as all applicants have had an opportunity to try out.

Record Keeping of the Recruitment Process

At this busy time, simple record keeping is of utmost importance. Three simple forms have been developed that work well --an individual applicant's card onto which ratings and comments can be recorded, a daily check-in sheet listing the names of all persons seen individually and giving their ratings, and a recruitment progress report sheet (see Appendix A). Ratings are based on the impressions from the personal interview and on the quality of the try-out interviews. If kept up to date, this system provides the necessary at-a-glance picture of progress during the recruitment process.

Hiring Decisions

Qualifying Criteria

The criterion that is an absolute necessity for qualification as an interviewer is that the applicant be a resident of the target area. Therefore, addresses must be checked before a person is even invited to an orientation meeting.

A second criterion that is strongly recommended is the establishment of a lower age limit of twenty-one. Most people under twenty-one are not mature enough to give the respondent the confidence necessary to make it possible to conduct a valid interview. Obviously, exceptions are possible, but they should be given careful thought. There seems little need for an upper age limit, persons who have the physical stamina and can meet the other requirements of interviewing are not too old for the job, no matter what their chronological age.

Another qualification is a personable appearance so that respondents will feel comfortable letting the interviewer into their homes.

Should the applicant's sex be a consideration? Our answer is "yes," but in relation to the subject matter of the survey and the particular sample of respondents. The questionnaires for the base-line health surveys were designed so that the person best informed about the health care of the household members could be the respondent for the entire household. This tended to be the female head or the wife of the head of the household. The interview included questions about family planning and birth control. We therefore assumed that it was easier for women to answer such questions from women interviewers. Experience on other surveys over the years has alerted us to the fact that, all things being equal, people are more likely to open the door to a woman than to a man. Women interviewers are also more likely than men to have interviewing as their only job commitment. Combining all these factors, NORC tended to hire more women than men as interviewers for the health center surveys.[1] Some men, of course, were able to establish excellent rapport with respondents, particularly in the single-male households. We should also point out that in some areas one might not wish to send women out to interview by themselves. In that case, men interviewers or male escorts are a good solution. On surveys where the respondents are primarily males, it would probably be wise to hire a greater number of male interviewers.

Other criteria for a good interviewer, such as good physical health, ability to read and write, availability, and interest both in other people and in the job, have been mentioned earlier. Each applicant is evaluated on the various qualifying criteria.

---

[1]Throughout this volume, we assume that most interviewers are women and shall therefore refer to them as such.

Characteristics of the Target Area

One additional consideration in making the hiring decisions is the racial or ethnic composition of the target area. Presumably this has been taken into account in the recruiting process so that some persons from each major racial or ethnic group will be represented among the applicants. Applicants tend not to be distributed proportionately, however, and one may have to make special efforts to recruit some applicants from a small but nonetheless significant group within the community. Occasionally, all efforts in that direction fail, and a decision will then have to be made on whether to send someone to interview a person from a different racial or ethnic group than her own or whether to recruit an interviewer from outside the target area. When the respondents speak English, the decision usually can be to send an interviewer from a different racial or ethnic group, but if language is a factor (as it was with some Yiddish-speaking respondents in Bedford-Crown), an interviewer, even from outside the community, who can speak the language may be the answer. Another constructive arrangement was worked out in the Red Hook area. Interpreters were hired to introduce the interviewer (in Italian), but the interview itself was conducted by a trained black interviewer. A third possibility is a combination of a local community interviewer and an interpreter from outside the community.

There are probably other solutions to these and similar problems, but the point we want to make here is that the characteristics of the target area must be kept in mind when making hiring decisions.

The Number of Interviewers To Hire

It is usually wise to hire a few (perhaps 20 to 33 per cent) more qualified candidates than absolutely necessary, since there is bound to be attrition on any interviewing staff. If many more candidates qualify than are needed, some will have to be told that they qualify but cannot be hired at this time. If the applicants have self-selected themselves out at the predicted rate, those left can probably all be hired and trained.[2] The possibility also exists, of course, that even after many orientation meetings, there will not be enough qualified candidates, and additional recruiting will have to be done.

To determine how many interviewers should be hired for a survey that uses a questionnaire of the length and complexity of those used in the health center surveys (see Appendix D) and that employs the strict area probability sampling method, we recommend the following formula:

$$N \div (T \times C) = I$$

where N = the total number of addresses in the sample,

T = the number of weeks to be allowed for the field period,

C = the average number of households an interviewer can contact per week,

I = the minimum number of interviewers to hire.

The formula would work as follows: assume that you have an original sample size of 2,000, that you want to complete field work in approximately eight weeks, and that an interviewer can contact an average of five households per week. Substituting $N = 2{,}000$, $T = 8$, and $C = 5$ in the formula, you have $2{,}000 \div (8 \times 5) = 50$. Hence, fifty is the minimum number of interviewers to hire. NORC experience indicates that in very large urban areas, such as New York, Washington, and Boston, attrition is higher than average and it is advisable to begin with about

---

[2] Only about 40 to 50 per cent of those attending orientation meetings actually go through the try-out process.

sixty interviewers for a survey of this magnitude and to allow twelve rather than eight weeks for the field period.

The Final Hiring Process

Throughout the recruitment and selection period, records should be kept of each applicant seen, as discussed earlier. When all applicants have been interviewed and the supervisor is ready to make the final hiring decisions (or to submit her recommendations to a board or committee of the health center for approval, if that is necessary), she should review her records and decide on which persons to hire. Each of the accepted applicants should then be sent a letter telling her that she has been hired, and giving the time and place of the first training session that she is to attend. Applicants who are rejected should also receive letters giving some explanation of why they were not hired. (See Appendix A for an example of each kind of letter.)

Required Time for Recruitment and Selection of Interviewing Staff

As we shall see in Chapter IV, the timing of this process should be coordinated with the preparation of the questionnaire and other interview materials so that both tasks are completed at about the same time. The entire recruitment and selection period will take from six to eight weeks. We present below a step-by-step outline of the recruitment and selection process and a chart indicating how these steps overlap.

1. Compile lists of community residents who are looking for work and who might be interested in an interviewing job.

2. Notify such persons of the survey and of the fact that interviewer applicants are being invited to orientation meetings to learn more about the job.

3. Establish a record-keeping system of the recruitment and selection process in order to keep track of the progress on a daily basis.

4. Hold orientation meetings to acquaint possible applicants with the nature of the survey, the health center, and the job of interviewer, and to distribute try-out kits.

5. Conduct individual personal interviews with applicants when they have completed the try-out interviews.

6. Make hiring decisions on the basis of the impressions in the personal interview, information on the application form, and the quality of the try-out interviews.

7. Notify all applicants of your decision, whether or not they have been hired.

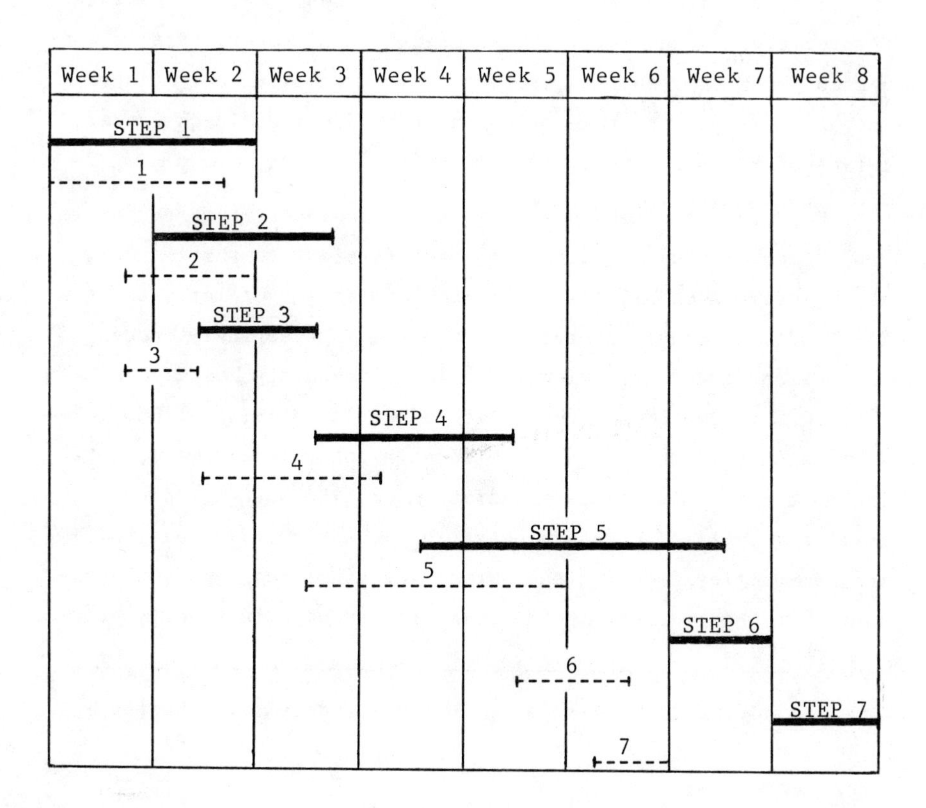

Hiring Field Listers

Although most applicants will be notified at the end of the hiring process whether they have been accepted or rejected, there is a specific exception to this. The field listing of the area, which must be done if a strict area probability sample is to be drawn, has to occur several weeks prior to the beginning of field work and before the interviewer training sessions. Some particularly bright and eager applicants (who can be spotted fairly quickly and easily) should be hired immediately and trained to do the field listing before the general training sessions for interviewing begin.[3]

Demographic Characteristics of Interviewers

The recruitment and selection procedures discussed in this chapter are, by and large, those used by NORC supervisors in connection with the health center studies in Brooklyn and Atlanta. In Table II.2 we can take a look at some demographic characteristics of the three interviewing staffs.

Note that the median age of interviewers on these three health center studies ranges from twenty-eight to thirty-two, which is considerably lower than the median age of forty-three for NORC's national interviewing staff. Interestingly enough, the median age of interviewers in the Five-County Health Survey that NORC conducted for the Office of Health Affairs of OEO in Wisconsin was forty-two. The Wisconsin interviewers were, for the most part, middle-class ladies, much like NORC's typical rural and small-town interviewers, but clearly indigenous to the communities in which the survey was conducted. It would appear that when recruiting for community surveys in poverty areas

---

[3] Listing will be discussed in greater detail in Chapter III.

TABLE II.2

SELECTED DEMOGRAPHIC CHARACTERISTICS OF INTERVIEWERS

Selected Characteristics	Atlanta	Bedford-Crown	Red Hook
Total number of interviewers	28	56	50[a]
Age:			
20 or under	-	2	8
21-30	9	30	19
31-50	18	19	21
51-64	-	5	2
65 or over	1	-	-
Median age	32	28	28
Sex:			
Male.	1	9	7
Female	27	47	43
Education:			
No high school	2	1	-
Some high school	11	21	17
High school graduate . .	14	19	23
Some college	1	15	2
College graduate	-	-	1
NA	-	-	7
Employment status on application:			
Unemployed	24	39	42
Part time	4	6	1
Full time	-	11	4
NA	-	-	3

[a]Records on the other two interviewers in Red Hook have been replaced and hence are not included here.

of large cities, younger people who are looking for a full-time or close to full-time work are more likely to apply and qualify.

The preponderance of females among the interviewers is due, of course, to NORC's feeling that, for the most part, women would be better suited than men to interview on these studies.

When we consider the interviewers' education, we see that on the average 39 per cent of the interviewers on the three health center studies had not completed high school, and in Atlanta the figure was 46 per cent. Thus, Table II.2 clearly indicates that formal education was not one of the criteria NORC used in the selection of interviewers.

The results of the heavy emphasis that NORC placed on hiring people who were unemployed at the time can be seen in the last section of the table. On the average, 78 per cent of the interviewers on the three studies had been unemployed, and in Atlanta the figure was 86 per cent with the remaining 14 per cent having had only part-time work.

Table II.2 would seem to indicate that if one makes a concerted effort to hire people who are unemployed, are young, and have enough education to read and write as required, one can indeed find them. In the following chapters we shall try to show how well they worked out once they were hired.

CHAPTER III

DRAWING THE SAMPLE

Implications of the Full Probability Sample

In any community survey, the sample of residents can be drawn in a variety of ways, depending on the requirements of the analysis and the availability of funds. For the health center surveys, it was decided by the various neighborhood health centers, NORC, and the Office of Health Affairs of OEO that a full probability sample of the target area population was necessary. The considerable funds required for this sampling method were included in the contract funding. Interviewing procedures, of necessity, are based heavily on the particular sampling method to be used. The discussions in this volume dealing with training interviewers, field listing, and field experiences are therefore based on the fact that the survey designs called for a full area probability sample.

Full probability samples of the noninstitutionalized civilian population of target areas can be drawn from complete lists of households of such areas. In the areas discussed here, such lists were not available, were outdated, or were incomplete. Thus, in drawing a sample of the target areas by standard probability sampling methods, census blocks were used as the primary sampling units.[1] For each block selected, all dwelling units

---

[1]For a detailed description of the process, see William C. Richardson, Red Hook Neighborhood Health Center Survey, Brooklyn, New York (Chicago: National Opinion Research Center, August, 1969), Appendix III.

were field listed. From these listings, specific dwelling units were selected for interview, again by standard probability sampling methods.[2]

The high cost of using the full probability sampling method is generated during the interviewing period because once the specific dwelling unit (DU) has been selected, no substitutions are permissible--that is, an interview (or perhaps more than one) is required at each DU in the sample. This implies call-backs at DUs where no one is home, where the occupant claims to be too busy, too ill, or refuses, or where all the information cannot be ascertained from the person who is at home when the interviewer first calls. The aim of the researcher who will use and analyze the interview data is always 100 per cent completion of the assigned sample. This is usually considered an ideal, but impossible, goal; but every effort should be made in the field to approach it within the limits of the funds available. Unless

---

[2]On one of the health center surveys (Mission Neighborhood Health Center area of San Francisco), NORC's sampling department drew the sample from the city directory instead of listing in the field. When this is done, one must institute a rather complicated system of checking for dwelling units that may have been missed by the directory. Many commercial establishments that contain no dwelling units are listed in the directory. Our conclusion was that it would have been better to have field listed, particularly in view of interviewer morale (they became discouraged when many assigned addresses turn out not to be dwelling units). It would be difficult to determine whether or not the use of an already existing list saved money in the long run due to the many complications that developed from this not-made-to-order listing.

In the case of another health center survey, NORC was able to draw the sample using the cards prepared by the Census Bureau from a just-completed census of the town. In fact, NORC recruited and trained some of the interviewers who worked on the census before beginning the health survey. The census lists, in return, were made available to us for the health survey. This proved most successful, but such fortuitous timing and dovetailing is probably very rare.

really unusual circumstances prevail, 80 per cent completion is considered a reasonable minimum. In the first three studies that NORC conducted in health center target areas, we were able to achieve somewhat above that--Atlanta, 91 per cent; Bedford-Crown, 81 per cent; and Red Hook, 82 per cent. Since interviewing costs include travel time, locating and waiting, and editing time, in addition to the time actually spent in the interview situation, one can readily see why the call-back requirement can add considerably to the cost of the interview.

Field Listing for the Full Probability Sample

Listing Materials

The standard probability sampling techniques call for a prelisting of the blocks or segments that have been drawn as the primary sampling units. We have found it best to provide each lister with a map that has the sampled block outlined in a special color. A duplicate of that map is kept by the supervisor. Attached to it are blank Dwelling Unit Listing Sheets (see Appendix C). An instruction manual, "How To List for an Area Sample," is also given to the interviewer (see Appendix C).

Who Are the Listers?

For timing as well as logical reasons, applicants who are particularly bright and among the first to apply and complete the hiring requirements are invited to join the training class for listers. Obviously the listing must be done, checked, and corrected (if necessary), and the specific DUs drawn before the interviewing assignments can be made. Early applicants tend to be more highly motivated, which is the reason they were early applicants in the first place. While there is always some variation, they usually learn listing quickly and thoroughly and do a competent job in a fairly short time. They can start the field listing while other interviewer applicants are being processed and should have finished the listing before training classes for interviewing begin.

Training the Listers

Learning how to field list requires some classroom discussion and some home study. The crucial part of training, however, is experience in the field. We recommend that after the listers have studied the instruction manual at home, they spend a short time (perhaps one or two hours) in the classroom with questions and answers based on the manual. The trainer should then take the listers into the field and actually list a block, explaining to the group what is being done, including in what order and in what detail each address should be listed. Trainees can take a turn at listing a few DUs and explain what they are doing. They should receive praise for listing correctly or constructive criticism on errors. In this fashion the entire group can benefit from individual actions, be they right or wrong, since all errors can be corrected immediately. The number of times that the trainer will take the group out for this kind of training depends on how quickly the group learns. It may be wise to start the next stage sooner with some listers than with others. The supervisor doing the training and observing is the best judge of this.

If the trainer feels that it would be helpful, the next stage can involve pairing the listers--a more confident, quick learner with a less self-assured one. Pairs of listers should receive small assignments, which should be reviewed in the office as soon as they are completed. In this way the supervisor can review the listed segments with each pair of trainees, thereby insuring that an accurate list is developed from which the sample will be drawn and that the listers receive additional help and instruction if needed.

The last stage of training the listers consists of ongoing training once each lister has a separate assignment. Listers should come into the office each day, bringing with them the previous day's work. Either the work should be reviewed immediately, or if supervisory time does not permit, it should be reviewed during the day and any questions should be discussed with the lister the next day. Repeated trips to the field for correction become discouraging to almost anyone. Listers who, even with ongoing training and close supervision, are found to have little aptitude for listing should be relieved of further work on this part of the survey. The final result from such a lister could affect the total accuracy of the listing and is therefore inefficient to the survey team and unrewarding to the lister. Such a lister might still be encouraged to join the first class in interviewer training, if the supervisor feels that she has a chance for success as an interviewer.

Supervision of the Listing Operation

The accuracy of the listing affects the selection of the sample DUs and later the task of the interviewer who must check to make certain that no DUs in her assigned areas have been missed. Therefore, the supervisor should work closely with listers until she is confident that they can do well on their own. An actual spot-checking in the field of a sample of the listed segments is necessary. This can be done by an assistant supervisor or a more experienced interviewer or lister. If no discrepancies are found, one can feel comfortable about the accuracy of the listing. If discrepancies do occur, they should be resolved by the supervisor and the erring listers should be helped to see the problem and correct it.

Supervisors should be available to answer questions as they arise. Sometimes a lister will call from the field to get a resolution to a problem that can be explained on the phone.

Other listers bring their problems into the office. All should receive quick, careful, and complete answers to their questions. Care must be taken to make it clear to the listers that no question is foolish and that the way to learn is to talk to the supervisors and to refer often to the written instructions. Some will need more reassurance than others, and it is the supervisor's job to provide it.

Depending on the complexity of the housing structures in the areas, the listing operation can take anywhere from twenty-five to forty-two man hours per 1,000 DUs and may require anywhere from one to three supervisors.[3]

---

[3] In Atlanta the total listing consisted of 6,648 dwelling units, which were listed by fourteen listers in approximately seven days. One supervisor worked with the listers. The first three days included classroom instruction plus field listing in "practice" blocks. The last four days were spent in actually listing the sample blocks. The housing in the target area consisted primarily of small private houses, some larger houses converted to several dwelling units, one city project, and a few low- and middle-income private apartment developments. For the most part, few problems were encountered in listing.

In the Bedford-Crown area of Brooklyn, fifteen listers and three supervisors required approximately fourteen days to list 40,000 dwelling units. Only the first day was devoted to classroom instruction, and even that day included some group field experience. Beginning on the second day, all listing done in the field was in actual sample blocks. The housing in this target area consisted of about one-third brownstones, one-third apartment buildings, two of which were large city housing projects, one-sixth dwelling units over stores, and one-sixth single-family houses. Numerous problems were encountered in listing the area, including the fact that a local "vigilante" group cooperating with the police told one lister that the area was not safe without a local escort; front doors of brownstones were locked, making it impossible to determine how many DUs were there. Many apartments had been subdivided, a fact that was not always apparent from the doorbells or mailboxes in the hallway.

In the Red Hook area of Brooklyn, six listers and one supervisor accomplished the task of listing 7,134 dwelling units in

An additional duty of the survey supervisor at this time might be the establishment of working relations with the police and local block "vigilante" groups (if they exist) to provide safety for the listers while they are in difficult or dangerous areas. Listers should always be provided with proper identification cards or letters, preferably cards with photographs.

---

six days. As in Bedford-Crown, field listing in the group began in actual sample blocks. One reason the listing was accomplished so quickly in this area is that a very large number of the DUs were in the city housing project, which was listed entirely from project records. The remainder of the area consisted primarily of small single-family houses. No listing difficulties were encountered.

CHAPTER IV

INTERVIEWER TRAINING

Goals of the Training Program

As in any educational venture, it is important in the training of interviewers to have clearly in mind precisely what is to be achieved by the training. The survey in question provides some obvious answers. Interviewers must be trained in general interviewing techniques and in how to apply these to the specific survey. The selection of the interviewing staff from among residents of a health center target area suggests additional training objectives. Based on the figures in Table II.2, we can see that only 19 per cent of the Bedford-Crown interviewers, 8 per cent of the Red Hook interviewers, and none of the Atlanta interviewers had full-time employment at the time they were hired for the interviewing job. We had made an effort to recruit persons who were unemployed and gave preference to such applicants. About 40 per cent of all these interviewers had never finished high school; another 42 per cent had no education beyond high school. If the interviewer training program is comprehensive enough, it can provide an opportunity for the participants to gain general marketable skills for a variety of jobs after the survey has been completed, in addition to specific preparation for interviewing.

Content of the Training

The important thing in considering the content of the training program is to cover all necessary material but at the same time to gear the training to the particular group. We present here an outline of a comprehensive training program for interviewers on a neighborhood health center study. This is not a schedule, and the order of presentation should be adapted to the particular group.

I. General Information about Surveys

- Overview of social research and its uses
- Steps in conducting a survey
- Overview of sampling and why it is done

II. Ethics of Research

- Confidentiality of all information gathered on surveys
- Anonymity of respondents
- Faithful reporting by interviewer

III. General Information about the Health Center and This Survey

- Short orientation on the health center's departments if their heads have been appointed
- How the survey will benefit the community

IV. Preparing To Go into the Field

- Positive attitude
- Proper dress
- Voice appeal

V. The Approach

- Introducing yourself
- Use of identification card
- How to handle yourself with persons who are uncomfortable, suspicious, or otherwise reluctant at the door
- Gaining respondent's cooperation

VI. Setting the Stage

- Establishing rapport
- Obtaining privacy for the interview
- Finding adequate seating in order to write
- Maintaining a professional manner
- Setting the respondent at ease

VII. Interviewing Technique

- Asking the questions as they are printed and in proper order
- Verbatim recording
- How and when to probe
- How to end the interview

VIII. Sampling Instructions for This Area Probability Sample

IX. Administrative Details

- Payment policies and procedures
- How to fill out time and expense reports
- When to report to the office for conference
- When and how to turn in completed work

X. Role-playing Practice on Try-Out Questionnaires, and Discussion of Problems That Arose in Try-Out Interviews

XI. Role-playing Practice on Actual Survey Questionnaire

XII. Discussion of All Survey Materials and Instructions in Their Use

XIII. Discussion of Validation and its Public Relations Function

XIV. Review of the Interviewer's Role in the Research Process

Timing of the Beginning of Training

Training should be scheduled to begin when the survey materials are ready and available. It is demoralizing to both the trainees and the trainer to be ready to work on the actual questionnaire only to find that the shipment of survey materials has not arrived. Since the beginning of training usually is also the beginning of payment for the trainees, it is not easy to "lay off" the training class while waiting for the questionnaires and other materials. Our recommendation is to base the timing for the beginning of recruitment on progress with the questionnaire. As we outlined in Chapter II, the recruitment and selection process requires from six to eight weeks. It is usually during this same period of time that the questionnaires, interviewer instructions, various forms, and other materials are in preparation. If one can pin down the specific date by which printed materials will be available, one can then count back six to eight weeks (depending on what is known about the community) and begin recruiting at that time. This avoids the necessity of delaying the beginning of training once the trainees are ready. It should be pointed out that delaying the training period usually means additional costs in manpower and money. Some trainees, who might have become good interviewers but who need income immediately, accept other employment; others become discouraged and drop out. The supervisor must then recruit replacements.

Length of the Training Period

In the first three health center surveys conducted by NORC, the amount of time actually spent by individual trainees in formal training sessions ranged from ten to over fifty hours. It should be pointed out that NORC was experimenting with a number of different training formats in these early surveys, with a view toward developing sufficient experience to make some recommendations. In the case of Atlanta, for example, some of the trainees received more than fifty hours of training. At the other extreme, we experimented in Red Hook with giving the absolute minimum of classroom instruction and instead devoted a greater number of supervisory staff and hours to working individually with the interviewers as they returned either with their completed interviews or with the field experiences that prevented them from interviewing. In a sense, then, the ten hours of formal group classroom training was extended on an individual basis, with more supervisory staff being available to the interviewers.

Depending again on the number of trainers available and on the particular group of trainees, we recommend from thirty to forty hours of group classroom training. This training can be accomplished either in half days spread over a two-week period or full days spread over the period of one week. We prefer the half-day, two-week arrangement since it is then possible to assign some home-study exercises such as a practice interview or studying a map. Home study, in general, can be an important part of the training. It enables each trainee to review what has happened in class at her own speed and to bring to the next class questions that arise from such a review.

Size of the Training Group

Training classes, as is the case with most learning situations, tend to be most productive when they are small enough to allow the trainer to observe each trainee and large enough to provide a variety of peers who can learn from and with each other. Depending on the trainer and the particular group of trainees, this can be anywhere from eight to fifteen persons. Some trainers function best in a fairly large group and are able to involve an entire group of up to fifteen trainees in active participation. Other trainers work best with a small group and find that learning is more likely to take place if only a few trainees are in the group. The size of the group can also be geared to what is felt might be best for a particular group of trainees. For example, we would suggest small groups for trainees who may be particularly timid. The survey supervisor should determine the appropriate size of the training group or groups.

Number of Trainers

There is no rigid answer to the number of trainers required. NORC has assigned as many as five experienced trainers to work with a group of trainees or as few as one unusually well qualified trainer. When only one trainer is available, the number of trainees per training class and the number of training days have to be greater. Two or three trainers for a two-week period would be ideal. The division of labor between the trainers depends on the skills and specializations of each. If the trainers are approximately equally qualified, it might be best to divide the trainees into three smaller groups and assign each small group to one trainer for the entire period. Alternatively, each trainer might move from group to group, working on a specific aspect of the training in which the trainer specializes.

Resource People as an Aid to Training

During the training period, interviewers will be exposed to many different aspects of interviewing and to the techniques that apply to these aspects. They should also gain some understanding of the purpose of the survey on which they will work and they should learn something about their employer, the neighborhood health center. Even if the health center is only in a formative stage, someone--be it the administrator, the medical director, the community organizer, or the training director--should talk to the trainees at some point during their training about the health center, its functions, when it will provide services, and to whom.

The local person most involved in the survey, perhaps one of the medical staff or the research director, would be a good person to speak to the group, discussing the reasons for doing a survey, what will be done with the data that the interviewers collect, how the survey information will be useful in the planning of services, etc. It may also be wise to have someone from the payroll department talk to the group about payment procedures, employee rules, and other aspects of their role as employees of the health center. As mentioned earlier, if the health center is already established, a short visit from each department head would be a useful addition to the training meetings.

The Physical Setting

There is general agreement among NORC trainers that the ideal arrangement for training sessions is a large conference room that is well ventilated and well lighted. Such a room is not always readily available but is certainly worth expending some effort to find. If the trainees are crowded, uncomfortable, or have trouble seeing or hearing, they are less able to get the most out of their training. If training is being conducted in the summer and the room is not air conditioned, every effort should be made to secure fans, and training sessions should be held as early in the day as possible.

A long table (or tables) and the chairs might be arranged in a square or T-shape. In any case, the seating should be arranged so that the trainer can be seen by all the trainees, they can all see each other, and the trainer can observe all of them.

Visual Aids for Training

A blackboard is almost a necessity and certainly one of the most flexible of visual aids. All the NORC trainers found it to be an indispensable tool. Opaque projectors are also convenient since they enable one to project almost any document onto a screen.

Other more mundane visual aids are the materials for the survey.[1] In the case of forms, examples can be drawn up and distributed so that the trainees each have their own copies. The questionnaires themselves become visual aids in order to point out specific examples of questions, skip instructions, or format. The trainees should each have their own copies of the questionnaires so that they can find the examples, make notes on their own copies, and generally follow the trainer's discussion.

The administrative specifications for the survey (see General and Administrative Instructions in Appendix D) provide some basic reading material on the way in which interviewers do their jobs. After the initial reading, these "spex" serve more as a reference document than as a visual training-aid. The Question-by-Question Specifications, however, are a visual training-aid when the class has progressed to the point where they actually work on the survey questionnaire. As can be seen in the sample in Appendix D, these instructions provide the rationale for how to ask the questions in the survey or give further instructions. We have found that writing such instructions directly on a copy of the questionnaire, as is the case with the main questionnaire in Appendix D, has a considerable advantage over the traditional survey research practice of a separate booklet of instructions. Trainees and experienced interviewers alike indicate that it makes their job of studying the questionnaire much easier. Any additional information can be given in the separate Question-by-Question Specifications Supplement.

---

[1]Examples of the types of forms, questionnaires, and specifications that might be used by the interviewers in a health center survey are presented in Appendix D.

Scheduling the Training

Training sessions should be scheduled so that they accommodate the participants to the greatest extent possible. There are a number of things to consider in scheduling.

Season of the Year

In the winter, one might wish to allow more time for people to arrive in the morning due to unpredictable, inclement weather. Sessions probably should be scheduled to begin at 9:30 or 10:00 A.M.

In the summer, particularly if the meeting room is not air conditioned, start sessions at 8:00 or 8:30 A.M. and try to finish by noon.

Availability of Trainer(s)

If more than one trainer is available, schedule sessions in such a way that each is at his or her best when doing the training.

If one trainer will train at all sessions, give consideration to the needs of that person. Try to accommodate the trainer within the constraints of the time and space set aside for training.

Availability of the Trainees

If some of the trainees have other employment, you might want to schedule a number of evening and weekend sessions for those who are employed elsewhere during the day. It may take a greater number of training hours all together for such a group since they will already be fatigued by the time they arrive for their sessions.

If trainees are available during the day, a good way to schedule training is:

9:00 A.M. - 12:00 Noon
12:45 P.M. - 2:30 P.M.

This allows mothers of school children to get them off in the morning and be home again before the children arrive home from school in the afternoon. Approximately an hour and a quarter of home study can be assigned each day. In this way, interviewers will receive a total of six hours of training a day, and it should be possible to complete training in one week.

Another possibility, if a two-week training schedule seems preferable, would look as follows:

9:00 A.M. - 12:00 Noon in training class
One hour of home study each day for two weeks

This would give the trainees thirty classroom hours and ten home-study hours over a two-week period.

If you have two daytime training groups, you could adopt the two-week schedule suggested above. During the first week have group A come from 9:00 A.M. to noon and group B come from 1:00 P.M. to 4:00 P.M. During the second week you could reverse the schedule and have group A come in the afternoon and group B in the morning. Each group would have one hour of home study each day for the two weeks. With such a tight schedule, we would recommend a minimum of two trainers.

Educational Level of the Trainees

The lower the educational level of the group of trainees, the greater the total time that should be allowed for the training period. For example, 63 per cent of the trainees in Brooklyn had completed high school, while only 54 per cent of the Atlanta group were high school graduates. Therefore, it was necessary to have a longer training period in Atlanta than in either Bedford-Crown or Red Hook.

Availability of Space

Sometimes a meeting room is available for the survey group at only certain times of the day or certain days of the week. If considered early enough, one could certainly adapt the training schedule to such limitations.

Some Guidelines for the Trainer

When planning for a training period, specifics of the community and the study should be taken into consideration, and we would hope that the outline presented below would be appropriately amplified. The following are some basic guidelines for the trainer:

1. Introduce yourself at the beginning of the first session, and allow enough time for the trainees to introduce themselves.

2. Learn the names of all trainees and remember them. Call on individuals by name.

3. Have an ample supply of note paper and pencils available so each trainee can have some.

4. Start the training by discussing those things that are usually uppermost in the minds of trainees:

   How many hours a week am I supposed to work?
   Do I have to work set hours?
   How long will the training take?
   Why is this study being done?
   Where will I be interviewing?
   Whom do I have to interview?
   How long will this job last?
   How and when will I get paid?

5. Keep an agenda in front of you of all items you want to cover each day, but don't be rigid about the order in which they are covered.

6. A good opener is a discussion of the experiences that trainees encountered while doing their try-out interviews. Often

the questions raised by such a discussion will provide enough material for the entire first session. Allow members of the group to volunteer ways in which a particular problem might have been solved more satisfactorily. Set a tone at that first meeting of a working-together on the part of the group--a team operation.

7. View your role as one of helping people do their best rather than finding fault with what they do or say. The trainer should reinforce correct answers or behavior when possible and help trainees understand how to handle situations that confuse them or that lend themselves to errors.

8. The atmosphere in the training class--like the atmosphere in the actual interview situation--should be businesslike but friendly. There should be an informal feeling that permits interviewers to ask questions or bring up problems for specific answers or for class discussion. When the members of the group actively participate, they can often learn from each other as much as or more than they would learn if the trainer were lecturing.

9. Know your material and how much you need to cover in a given session. In that way you can give direction but allow the group to discover answers for themselves, interjecting yourself only when wrong solutions or answers are offered.

10. Role-playing the interview situation is the best method for teaching good interviewing technique. The trainees can take turns playing the roles of respondent and interviewer. This method can be used to teach trainees how to approach a dwelling unit, how to make the initial introduction, and how to conduct the actual interview.

11. Occasionally the trainer can play the part of the respondent in order to present a difficult situation for the interviewer to solve. At times the trainer should play the part of the interviewer to illustrate a particular technique.

12. During the role-playing, all the other trainees except the one who is asking the questions and the one who is the respondent should be recording the responses. The trainer can observe (by walking around the table) whether anyone is having trouble in recording the responses. A useful exercise to highlight the importance of verbatim recording is to have each trainee read what she recorded in response to a given question.

13. Home study could consist of doing another practice interview, of reading some additional material, of finding answers to some specific questions, or anything that seems to require improvement for the particular group. The report of one NORC trainer in Atlanta provides a good illustration.

> In the process of training, it was clear that additional help was needed in pronunciation and vocabulary building, spelling, simple arithmetic and how to tell time and compute elapsed time.
>
> The Reading Center at Atlanta University loaned a language master machine and a tape recorder for the duration of the training period. The class selected the words with which they had pronunication difficulty or for which they wanted definitions. They were assigned sessions with the language master machine to aid in their pronunication of many wordes and phrases. They selected such words as the following: numerical, penury, destitution, indigent, semantics, decisive, fixtures, profitable, inherent, anonymous, synonym, recommended, psychiatrist, psychologist, influenced, activities, obvious, specialist, chiropractor, statistics, respondent and rapport.
>
> The class was assigned home study to look up each word in a dictionary and write a sentence including the word. We also spent time in learning to divide words into syllables and noting accent marks to aid in pronunication. To my amazement each trainee appeared at class the next day with a borrowed or owned dictionary. They enjoyed working with words and devoted serious attention to trying to improve their vocabularies. Although the sentences were poorly constructed in many instances, their understanding of the meaning of the words was evident.

Our Atlanta trainer continues in her discussion of classroom activities:

After they felt secure about my desire to help them, I tackled several bad speech habits which they were to eliminate entirely. These were "peoples," "childrings," and "axked." It became a rule that whenever the slip occurred the class would stop until it was corrected. This worked out not only in good humor but with good results.

In teaching how to probe open-ended questions, I decided to learn more about their individual interests and ambitions, as well as to give them experience in articulation. Some of the questions on which they probed each other were:

-If you could apply today for any job for which you feel qualified, which job would it be? (Probe: Why that one?)

-If you could get training free today for the job of your choice, which job would it be? (Probe: Why would you choose that one?)

-What do you think are the major problems facing the people in the Center's target area today? (Probe: What other major problems?)

-If you could send your eldest child to the college of your choice, which one would you select? (Probe: Why would you select that one?)

Another example of class work was the use of written tests to determine what the trainees had retained. The following is an example:

1. Tell me what you know about the program of the Comprehensive Health Center--such as, when it will open; whom it will serve; what it plans to do for the community; who is eligible for help; why every eligible person isn't going to be served when it first opens; and anything else you think of interest about the Center.

2. Now that you know something about the job of an interviewer, what do you think are <u>your own</u> strengths (or good points) for this?

3. What do you think are your weaknesses for this job?

4. Which part of the interviewer's job would you like to know more about, or have us work on more in class?

5. What is a respondent?

6. What is a precoded question?

7. What is an open-end question?

> Since only one trainee had any knowledge of the use of maps, a session was devoted to this. Maps were distributed and symbols explained. Several exercises were given to the trainees to illustrate the use of the maps. One trainee explained later that she had become lost on the outskirts of Atlanta, at first she cried, but then remembered her street map and was able to find her way back to familiar territory.
>
> Several sessions were devoted to arithmetic problems. Since the income questions on the survey are asked in terms of weekly, monthly and yearly amounts, interviewers had to learn how to translate any given amount into its proper terms. This required facility in adding, multiplying or dividing. Many of the trainees found it extremely difficult to remember long division, or which method to use to obtain the correct answer. Blackboard as well as home study assignments were given.
>
> The other computation which required much practice was elapsed time. For instance, if an interview began at 11:30 AM and ended at 2:15 PM, what was the elapsed time which was to be recorded at the end of the questionnaire? In the process of working on these problems, I learned that two trainees did not know how to tell time correctly. A big clock was drawn on the blackboard and simple clock reading instruction was given.

As a result of the arithmetic deficiencies that we found in Atlanta, the same trainer later developed a quiz to be given to training classes. An example of such a quiz, used for the first time in connection with the health center study in Charleston, South Carolina, can be found at the end of Appendix A.

For a general discussion of some of the other items included in the program outline given earlier in this chapter, see the first thirteen pages of the Specifications for Try-Out Questionnaire in Appendix A.

CHAPTER V

SUPERVISION OF THE FIELD WORK

Supervision of the field work on a health survey in a target area is conceptually no different from supervision of field work on any survey anywhere in the United States. The interviewers receive their assignments. They report back to the office on the progress of their work. This progress is monitored, and the quality of the work is controlled in the office. Ongoing training of the interviewers, or retraining when needed, is conducted by the supervisor or her editing staff. Problem cases are analyzed and decisions are made on whether future attempts to achieve the interview would be fruitful. A sample of the interviews are routinely validated from the office by a phone call or personal visit to the respondent. While we see no conceptual differences between neighborhood health center base-line surveys and surveys in general, we do see some operational differences.

Regardless of the survey involved, interviewers set their own pace and their own hours, as long as those hours match the hours when their designated respondents are available for interview. Interviewing is often lonely work, requiring resourcefulness, stamina, perseverance, punctuality, alertness, interest in others, and attention to detail, to mention just a few qualities. The health center interviewers are usually novices at interviewing, and in a good many instances also novices at dealing with the public, at performing written clerical tasks, and at working on their own. Therefore, they tend to need a great deal of support and encouragement in order to manage the difficult job they have to do. The remainder of this chapter is devoted to spelling out ways in which these novice interviewers can be helped to perform at their best to gather quality data and achieve a high response rate, all within the time period and budget allotted for the field work.

Making the Assignments

The reader will recall from Chapter III that geographic segments were field-listed. From these lists, the sampling department designates those dwelling units that fall into the sample. Before the actual field work begins, the interviewers, as a group, can participate in assignment preparation. This is essentially a clerical task of transferring the street address and other identifying information for each sample household from the Dwelling Unit Listing Sheet (see Appendix C) onto the Household Folder (see Appendix D), which will eventually contain all parts of the completed interview. For the purpose of getting the household folders prepared, the group can be divided into "writers," who write on an household folder the street address and other identifying information, and "proofreaders," who check the work of the "writers" for accuracy and legibility. The NORC trainer who supervised the Atlanta health center survey used this technique successfully and reports that it served the two-fold purpose of involving the interviewers more in the total survey operation and at the same time getting the clerical task accomplished. Care must be taken to explain to the interviewers that errors in copying will cause confusion in the field. Although the interviewers should be highly motivated to copy correctly since any folder may become part of their own assignment, they are inexperienced and supervisory staff must review the work carefully.

When all the folders have been prepared, the field work can be assigned. Each interviewer should receive an assignment of one segment--probably around five households. It is important to make assignments large enough so that the interviewer has a good chance to conduct an interview on each trip to the field (i.e., if no one is home at one household, she can go down the street to the next one) and small enough so that a novice interviewer can finish the assignment in a period of a week, or at least have been able to make an attempt at each assigned household. A further advantage of small assignments to new interviewers is the control that the supervisor has over the work flow. We know that new interviewers have a higher attrition rate at the beginning of a study--particularly if things happen to go poorly. The fewer cases a wavering interviewer has, the less confusion arises if her work must be reassigned because she leaves.

If the target area is spread out geographically, one should make an effort to assign cases in a way that minimizes the amount of travel time required for the interviewers. Those interviewers who will have to take public transportation should be assigned to segments easily accessible by public transportation. Interviewers should understand clearly that if they discover that they know a person in their assignment, they should turn that case back to the office for reassignment to another interviewer. This policy underscores the points made during the training period about confidentiality of the data.

Information about which sections of the sample area would make for easier interviewing is sometimes available prior to the beginning of field work. If such information can be ascertained, it is a good idea to give the interviewers their first assignments in the "easier" sections. In short, whatever one can do to pave the novice interviewer's way for her first field experience is well worth the effort. It has payoff in the higher morale of the interviewing staff, which encourages greater production, higher cooperation rates, and better quality interviews.

Record System in the Office

A large part of field supervision involves monitoring the work flow on a daily basis--knowing what has been assigned to whom, how much completed work is back in the office, how much has been returned incomplete, how much is still in the field, and how much is left to be assigned. The key to effective and efficient supervision of work flow lies in a good record-keeping system. Persons responsible for an operation usually like to design a system that will work best for them. We present here a system of record-keeping, components of which have worked well for NORC not only in connection with the health center surveys but also on other NORC projects.[1]

The system provides a master control of each case in the sample, and a separate control of what each interviewer has in her possession. Neither control would be sufficient by itself, but together they provide means for checking and balancing at any given moment.

The master control is organized by segment once the sample selection of specific dwelling units has been made. The Master Control Sheets (Log Form 1) are kept in segment order in a notebook.

The Interviewer Records (Log Form 2) are organized by interviewer name, either in manila folders (one for each interviewer)

---

[1] All record-keeping forms referred to in this section and instructions for using them can be found in Appendix E.

or in a notebook arranged alphabetically by the interviewers' last names.

The progress of the field work should be charted on a weekly basis, using the weekly Progress Report (Log Form 3). The information needed to prepare this report is on the master control sheets. Work sheets are generally used to record totals from each segment of the control sheet for each category called for on the progress report. Then these are totaled and entered on the progress report.

For a daily check on work progress, NORC has developed a Daily Take Record (Log Form 4), which provides at a glance the daily figure on the number of completed cases by interviewer, the total for the day, and the cumulative total.

The four forms briefly discussed here constitute the simplest and yet the most comprehensive system we have been able to devise for monitoring the work flow. Some of the subsequent sections of this chapter deal with ways of using the information in the record system to improve the quality and flow of work.

Interviewer Reporting

New interviewers generally require more and closer supervision than do experienced interviewers. As we saw in Table II.2, the interviewing staffs for the health center surveys tended to have limited formal education. What education they did have was often from schools where the quality of education was known to be less than good. Further, we were dealing with interviewers whose previous work experience did not prepare them in any way for the activities and tasks of interviewing. It was decided, therefore, that a daily reporting into the office would be a constructive use of the interviewers' time. Looking back, we still feel this to be the case and recommend that interviewers report to the office every day, at least until the supervisor on the scene decides otherwise. In the case of Atlanta, daily reporting was not difficult to achieve because in selecting the interviewers we made a conscious effort to give priority to the unemployed rather than the underemployed. The supervisor wrote in her report:

> Because of their availability, strict reporting rules were established in an effort to simulate regular work situations, rather than the more permissive schedule normally used by our NORC field workers. Each person was required to report daily either in person or by telephone, though they were not required to work an eight-hour day.

Office reporting can accomplish a two-fold purpose: (1) the interviewer can bring in completed work, ask any questions that trouble her, and discuss problem cases, and (2) the supervisor has an opportunity to review with the interviewer her work shortly after it has been edited, to give retraining where needed, and to provide encouragement at the right time. In addition, the daily reporting system provides the supervisor with an opportunity to learn why some interviewers are not producing completed interviews at the expected rate.

Most interviewers, particularly new ones, require considerable help in using their time efficiently. When the interviewer reports to the office, she is asked to bring with her the household folders for those cases that she has not yet completed. By looking at the record-of-calls section on the front of the folders, the supervisor can often spot problems and give suggestions to the interviewer on matters such as how to find people who have not been at home.

In discussing a completed interview, the interviewer may alert the supervisor to misunderstandings about some sections of the questionnaire or about a particular question. Such problems can be cleared up on the spot with the one interviewer, but the encounter also alerts the supervisor to the problem itself, which may be affecting other interviewers.

As the supervisor of Red Hook wrote:

> The credit for the high quality of interviewing should probably be ascribed to the individual conferences that were held with the interviewers immediately after they returned their early work. Neither was time allowed to elapse, nor were errors allowed to become habitual before speaking to an interviewer. . . . In general, it was the one-to-one relationship between interviewer and supervisor which was the key to understanding exactly what the interviewer did and did not grasp. Perhaps, too, there was something in the individual attention to which the interviewer responded favorably.

Quality Control

Quality of field-interviewing on surveys is controlled in four basic ways: (1) an editing staff in the survey office edits completed interviews and keeps records for feedback to the interviewers, (2) supervisor(s) and/or editors do ongoing training of the interviewers through individual or group conferences, (3) the supervisory personnel validate interviews from the office with a sample of the respondents, and (4) supervisors analyze problem cases and follow them up in an effort to achieve an acceptable completion rate. We shall discuss each of the four means of quality control separately and also give some indication of how they fit together.

Editing

The editing of completed questionnaires is a systematic review of the interviewers' work. NORC developed some editing guidelines (see memorandum in Appendix F) in an effort to standardize editing procedures. In reviewing or editing the completed questionnaires, editors look for inconsistencies in factual data, for incomplete answers to open-ended questions, for errors in following skip patterns, and most importantly, for missing data on "crucial" questions. The researcher will usually designate some questions as "crucial" since the lack of an answer to these questions means that the interview must be considered incomplete.

NORC's experience indicates that to be a good editor one must know the questionnaire and interviewer instructions thoroughly. It is therefore advisable to have the editors participate in the training sessions on the survey questionnaire. Experienced interviewers have the highest probability of performing well as editors. They know what the interviewer's job is all about. They can discuss the quality of an interviewer's questionnaires with her in a sympathetic way and thereby encourage the interviewer to improve her skills and techniques because she has not been "put down" by the editor.

Ongoing Training

By discussing the interviewers' questionnaires with them, the editor can serve an ongoing training function. It is possible, for example, to have certain interviewers report to a particular editor, who will have reviewed all their work and be able to discuss it with them. The editor is well advised to look simultaneously at more than one questionnaire from a given interviewer. In this way, repeated errors can be quickly spotted, retraining can take place, and the interviewer will be on the way to improvement. If patterns develop, with more than one or two interviewers making the same mistake or the same kind of mistake, the editor should call this to the attention of the supervisor, who can take steps to retrain all or part of the group in one portion of the questionnaire.

In addition to the assistance given by the editing staff, ongoing training or retraining is often done in the individual conferences that supervisors have with interviewers when they come in to report. Although they paid close attention in the group training sessions, many interviewers find that they do not really absorb it all until they have been out in the field and gained some experience. At that point, the individual or small conferences with the supervisor or editor are of most benefit. It is then that the interviewer can begin to ask the questions that she could not even formulate during the training sessions. This is the time for the supervisor to reinforce the earlier training--and now it can be done with examples supplied by the interviewers themselves. We quote again from our Atlanta supervisor:

> In addition to the (individual) conferences, a staff meeting was scheduled for each Friday at 1:30 to coincide with the payroll period. Those meetings consisted of a discussion of the most common errors being made, as well as a time to boost their morale and encourage the group by pointing up all the positives in the situation. If a particularly large number of interviews had been done that week, a reward party was given. It would consist of assorted fruits or soft drinks. The staff enjoyed the get togethers and rarely was anyone absent. In fact, one of the outstanding features of the Atlanta staff was their deep sense of responsibility and feeling of oneness with each other.

Validation

Validating interviews is the process of verifying with a random sample of respondents that the interview was actually conducted and that the data as recorded are accurate (see copy of Follow-up Interview Form in Appendix F). The researcher directing the survey usually makes the decision about what percentage of the respondents should receive follow-up or validation interviews.

The follow-up interview, which should take no longer than ten minutes, has several purposes. First, it serves a public relations purpose by giving the supervisory personnel an opportunity to thank the respondent for his contribution of time and interest and by giving the respondent a chance to ask questions or make comments about the survey. It serves the validation purpose in that answers to the questions asked will presumably confirm answers given earlier to the interviewers, thereby giving the study director some systematic evidence that he is receiving valid data. Finally, it serves a quality-control purpose because when an interviewer's work does not check out, the supervisor is quickly alerted to a problem and can take appropriate action.

If the respondent claims he was not interviewed, or gives answers considerably different from those written on the original questionnaire, the next step is to validate 100 per cent of that particular interviewer's work since the word of one respondent cannot be considered sufficient evidence of falsification. If, after a thorough check, it appears that falsification did occur, the interviewer should be relieved of all assignments and dismissed. The falsified interviews cannot be used, and those cases must be reassigned for interview. If there are differences between the original and the follow-up interview that are attributable not to falsification but to poor or sloppy work, the question is whether the interviewer is retrainable or should be dismissed. In either case, a conference with the interviewer is in order. If, as a result of the conference, the decision is to retrain, this should take place as quickly as possible, and all further work from that interviewer should be validated 100 per cent.

The clear caveat implied above is to start the validation process within a week or two of the beginning of field work. The sooner falsifications are discovered, the sooner appropriate actions can be taken. As completed questionnaires arrive in the office, some should be clearly designated "for validation" on a systematic basis, such as every fourth one from each interviewer. Those respondents who can be reached by phone should be called as soon after the original interview as possible; those with no phones should be assigned for a field visit from supervisory personnel. It is important that interviewers know that no one can get away with falsified interviews. Nothing is as helpful to the interviewers in the long run as the knowledge that they will not be allowed to cheat. Interviewers should be told that validation will be done on a random basis as a routine part of quality control. When inconsistencies or discrepancies are found, the supervisor should discuss them with the interviewer. On the positive side, the supervisor should bring to the interviewer's attention any comments from respondents that are flattering to the interviewer.

Starting the validation procedure at the very beginning of field work also insures that only a few days have elapsed between the original interview and the follow-up interview, an important factor in helping the respondent recall the interview and the interviewer.

From our experience on the neighborhood health center surveys, we learned that an all-important question to ask in follow-up interviews is whether or not the respondent actually lived in the assigned dwelling unit at the assigned address at the time of the original interview since there might have been a change in occupancy. We had omitted this question from early validation forms.

As a final warning on this topic, we quote from our Red Hook supervisor:

> In one case only two of about thirty-five completed cases (of one interviewer) validated. This case was that of an interviewer who was asked to pick up a lot of information that was missing from other people's interviews. The mistake was made of thinking that

since her own work had been validated, the rest of her work would also. The lesson to be learned is that validation must not be relaxed for any one at any time.

Problem Cases

Problem cases arise when the interviewer, for one reason or another, does not succeed in conducting an interview at an assigned household. The Non-Interview Report (see Appendix D) is the form that the interviewer uses to report a problem case to the office. The reason for non-interview is indicated on the NIR and reviewed by the supervisor. In the case of "not-at-home" households, the supervisor may be able to advise the interviewer about a better time to attempt a contact and then return the case to the interviewer.

Refusals, on the other hand, are usually reassigned to another interviewer. NORC experience indicates that collecting refusals in a separate folder and holding them there for a while is a good idea, at least at the beginning of the field work. Later on, when interviewers have gained self-confidence, and can more easily cope with difficult cases, there is sufficient time to reassign refusals. By the time the refusals are reassigned, the supervisor will know which interviewers enjoy and can rise to the challenge of converting refusals into completed cases. Interviewers who enjoy this type of challenge are usually successful at it. Such interviewers are easily recognized since they tend to produce few problem cases from their own assignments.

The weekly progress reports give the supervisor a good basis upon which to make decisions about following up on problem cases. The following hypothetical situation illustrates the kinds of actions a supervisor might consider: Suppose that six weeks of a ten-week field period are over. The completion rate at this point is 60 per cent, or 900 of 1,500 cases are complete.

There is every reason to believe that an additional 250 to 300 cases will be completed in the normal run of the next two or three weeks. What should be done about the 200 cases that are already NIRs? And what should be done with the 100 or so that will come in during the next couple of weeks as NIRs? Look carefully at the reasons for non-interview. Assign to interviewers all those cases that have a high probability of yielding an interview now, even though the original interviewer could not get one earlier. Use all information on the NIR plus all information you have about the interviewing staff to help you decide which interviewer has the best chance of completing a particular case. Send special letters to those persons who refused because they did not understand the purpose of the study. In the letter explain the survey clearly and indicate that an interviewer will call soon. Consider making some telephone appointments for the interviewers from the office, if that would seem to be useful. Send an interpreter along with the interviewer if the reason for non-interview was a language problem. Suppose that by this process 100 cases can be converted to completed interviews during that two- to three-week period, and only 240 of the original cases left in the field come in completed. You will have a total of 1,240 completed interviews at the end of the ninth week, or a completion rate of about 83 per cent. Now you will want to take a look at the 100 or so cases that came in as NIRs in the last couple of weeks and perhaps reassign some of them. Suppose the interviewers complete another 30. Now you will have 1,270 completed interviews and a completion rate of 85 per cent. Unless your budget still has money in it and you can get an extension on the field period, you had probably better call it quits. A completion rate of 85 per cent is quite respectable.

In general, an 80 per cent completion rate is considered acceptable. Anything less than that would have to have substantial documentation to explain the low rate. If there are reasons in the community for a low completion rate, it might be wise to have a statistician examine the figures and the distribution of non-interviews and determine whether the sample of respondents contains any systematic bias.

The need for an acceptable completion rate becomes clear when one considers that a sample has been drawn statistically to represent the total population. Whenever we let the individuals in the sample self-select themselves out of it, we are losing some of the representativeness of the sample. Some loss is tolerable, but a large loss will limit the statistical value of the inferences made from the replies of those who do respond. An important aspect of quality control in any field survey is to make sure that the completion rate is as high as possible within the limits of time, money, and human resources.

Payment Procedures

Interviewers are generally paid by the hour, based on the time and expense reports that they turn in each time they bring in completed work (see Interviewer's Time Report in Appendix B). They are instructed to charge for study time, travel time, interviewing time, editing time, and conference time in the office--in other words, for all time spent in connection with the survey. In addition, they may charge an agreed-upon amount per mile for distance traveled in their car or they may charge for the amount spent on public transportation. This type of payment procedure is most equitable for interviewers on this kind of interview since the length of time per interview varies with the number of household members and with the amount of illness in the household. Incentive increases in the hourly rate are strongly recommended after an agreed-upon number of interviews have been satisfactorily completed. Payroll departments of health centers, however, are usually not geared to this kind of payment procedure. In fact, problems with interviewer pay have occurred in one way or another on every health center survey in which NORC has been involved.

We recommend that someone from the health center be brought into the picture early. Discuss in detail the problems that interviewers face if they do not receive their checks on time. In some cases they will have expended their own funds, for which they must be reimbursed. They must know how often they will be paid and how much time lag will occur between turning in a time sheet and being paid for the work it represents. The supervisor must understand clearly what the payment policy of the health center will be before making any promises to interviewers. The supervisor in turn must do her best to meet the needs of both the business office and the interviewers.

CHAPTER VI

WHAT HAPPENS WHEN THE SURVEY IS FINISHED?

When the field work is satisfactorily brought to an end, interviewers who, after four to six months of new experiences and hard work, will be out of a job. In some instances they will have missed an opportunity for other employment in the community, or even the chance to become a health aide or clerical worker within the health center.

The OEO policy of providing new career ladders for persons living in the neighborhood health center target areas can receive reinforcement at this point with the provision of funds to enable the supervisor to be available as a resource person for approximately one month after the end of the field period. The incremental cost of building this into the original budget is small, and it allows someone who knows the interviewers to help them find employment or further training if that is what they wish.

Job Possibilities for the Interviewers

NORC asked the interviewers from some of the health center surveys to fill out an Interviewer Report Form at the end of the field period.[1] In response to the question, "Do you see interviewing as good training for another job?" the almost

---

[1] A copy of this form can be found in Appendix G. Forty-one interviewers completed this form--twenty-two from Atlanta and nineteen from Red Hook.

unanimous answer was "yes."[2] The distribution of responses to the follow-up question, "What kind of job?" is presented in Table VI.1.

TABLE VI.1

KIND OF JOB FOR WHICH INTERVIEWING IS SEEN AS GOOD TRAINING

Kind of Job	Number of Interviewers
Social work/group work/community work	16
Receptionist/personnel interviewer	9
Clerical or general office work	4
Health aide/health assistant/visiting nurse aide	3
Interviewing/other research work	3
Sales clerk	2
Total	37

All but four of these thirty-seven interviewers felt that interviewing had prepared them for jobs that have working with people as their major component. Responses to the question, "How did interviewing prepare you for it?" indicate that they had gained self-confidence and had benefited from interacting with respondents. The following are examples of answers to that question:

> Learning to understand people more.
>
> Interviewing prepared me for the job of personnel interviewer or receptionist by teaching me how to maintain rapport with people, by being able to keep on the track of what we're talking about and composure.

---

[2] Thirty-seven of the forty-one interviewers answered "yes," three answered "no," and one did not answer the question at all.

I was a little shy about talking to people at first. Now I can start talking first.

Made me sure of myself; most of all taught me how to talk with different types of people; also improved my speech.

Taught me how to approach people. Lose fear of them.

By getting out of the habit of being shy, and being direct.

Teach patience.

Dealing with people. It gave great insight toward dealing with all types of people. It gave me poise, confidence in myself.

As an interviewer I learn to observe people more. I am more aware of the people's needs in the community.

Fully enabled and prepared me to cope and adjust to any situation.

Now I have more confidence in myself. Have learned to understand people's reactions better.

It gave me the experience which all the jobs I have tried for wanted.

I understand more of the problems some people have and I won't be as shy about talking in group discussions as I once was.

Interviewing has taught me to have confidence in myself.

To meet and know how to deal with people and how to be patient.

How to talk with people and to get into their homes and how to keep their mind on what you be telling them.

In contrast to Table VI.1, Table VI.2 shows previous jobs held by the twenty-two Atlanta interviewers included in Table VI.1, plus eight additional persons hired for the Atlanta survey who either became part of the office staff or otherwise left the interviewing staff before the survey ended.

Interviewers apparently feel prepared to embark on new and more highly skilled career lines as a result of their training and interviewing experience. Some have gained enough self-confidence to seek new kinds of employment on their own; others are more timid and manage more easily if they can rely on the continued support of the supervisor they have come to trust.

TABLE VI.2

PRESENT OR PREVIOUS OCCUPATION OF ATLANTA INTERVIEWING STAFF AS OF MAY 24, 1968[a]

Occupation	Number of Interviewers
Office worker	8
Teacher assistant	2
Domestic worker	6
Factory worker	1
Food service worker	6
Laundry worker	3
Tailor	1
Postal clerk	1
Photo shop helper	1
Nursery helper	1
Total	30

[a]Before survey began.

The Role of the Supervisor

The supervisor, as we envision it, would remain in the community for a period of time after the survey was completed to serve as a resource person for the interviewers. She would have to expend some time and effort in gathering information from various persons in the local community and in the city as a whole. She would first have to become knowledgeable about job-training and employment opportunities in a wide variety of interest areas. Next she would have to contact employers by letter, on the phone, and in person to make them aware of the resource of personnel who will be available. She would then arrange for employment interviews with prospective employers, or plan meetings at which employers could meet a number of interviewers and discuss job possibilities with them. She could be available to the interviewers as a sounding board, to listen to their ideas and plans for themselves, and to offer practical suggestions. She could, in a sense, open doors for people who have previously had many of those doors closed to them.

A good description of positive results in helping the interviewers to find other employment when the survey is finished can be found in a report from Mrs. Fansayde Calloway, NORC's supervisor for the Atlanta survey (see Appendix H).

On a less positive note, it should be mentioned that we also experienced some negative attitudes toward the interviewing staff staff from personnel at some health centers. In at least one instance, in spite of NORC's painstaking efforts to point out the temporary nature of their job, interviewers felt that they had been misled by the health center into thinking that they would be able to count on permanent employment at the end of the interviewing job. It appeared that the interviewers were in fact given less than equal opportunity for slots in the health center training programs and other health center jobs. We cannot emphasize too strongly the extreme importance of giving no false assurances at any time. The trainers, supervisors, and health center staff share the responsibility of making clear that interviewing is a temporary job that ends when the field work is finished.

APPENDIX A

RECRUITING MATERIALS

SRS-4053
1968

NATIONAL OPINION RESEARCH CENTER
University of Chicago

MEMO TO INTERVIEWER APPLICANTS

CHARLES DREW NEIGHBORHOOD HEALTH CENTER

St. Mary's Hospital
1260 St. Marks Avenue
Brooklyn, N.Y.
467-6714

The following information is offered to help you decide whether you wish to apply as an interviewer on a study to be conducted in the Bedford Stuyvesant-Crown Heights area of Brooklyn.

1) About this study. This study will be conducted jointly by the Charles Drew Neighborhood Health Center and the National Opinion Research Center. We will be interviewing residents of the Bedford Stuyvesant-Crown Heights community about their families' health, their knowledge and use of various health services and general health attitudes.

2) About the Charles Drew Neighborhood Health Center. The Center has been established to bring much-needed health services into the community and to involve community residents in health-related jobs.

It was named for Dr. Charles Drew, a Negro physician who pioneered in the use and storage of whole blood, an achievement responsible for greatly advancing the field of health care.

The Center is funded by the Office of Economic Opportunity and the federal Department of Health, Education and Welfare.

3) About NORC. The National Opinion Research Center is a non-profit organization affiliated with the University of Chicago which conducts many kinds of surveys of interest to social scientists, foundations and government agencies. Recent surveys include: a study of the health needs and resources of older people, an inventory of the problems experienced by migrants and long-term residents living in metropolitan neighborhoods, and many others.

4) No previous interviewing experience is required. All candidates hired will be personally trained by the NORC Field Department.

5) The interviewer's job is to visit certain assigned homes to interview designated occupants, using printed questionnaires. During the interview, the interviewer records the respondent's answers by circling the appropriate code number on the questionnaire or by writing in the person's reply word-for-word. Then the interviewer edits each questionnaire to make sure it is all filled in accurately and clearly. Interviews will be about one hour in length.

6) Duration of interviewing. The interviewing period will be approximately two months, to begin about the middle of May 1968.

7) Hours of work and assignment size. Each interviewer must be available to work a minimum of 20 hours a week and should complete a total assignment of about 40 interviews. Those interviewers who have more available time will be expected to complete an additional number of interviews appropriate to their working hours. Interviewing will take place during the daytime as well as evenings and weekends.

8) Screening of applicants. In order to be considered for employment, each applicant will be required to conduct two brief interviews to help the Field Department measure his ability to do this work. Time spent on these "try-out" interviews is not reimbursable.

9) Training procedures. Applicants are selected for training on the basis of completed application, personal interview and the "try-out" interviews. Those who qualify will enter our training program.

The field interviewer, using the questionnaire, is a most important link between the planning and completion of any survey. In order to insure that each of our interviewers is thoroughly prepared and comfortable in the interviewing situation, NORC provides a very complete training program. We believe that professional skill in interviewing will be useful to you even after you have completed work on this survey. There will be approximately 20 hours of training time.

10) Pay arrangements. Interviewers will be paid on the basis of $2.20 per hour for all authorized time spent on assignments, including travel time. In addition, all necessary direct expenses (such as telephone calls and fare) are reimbursable. Payment for training time is at $1.75 an hour and is made after the interviewer has begun work on her assignment.

All payments to interviewers are made by the Charles Drew Neighborhood Health Center.

For further information, please telephone Mrs. Weisinger or Mrs. Phillips at 467-6714.

COVERING LETTER

COMPREHENSIVE HEALTH CENTER
1070 WASHINGTON STREET, S. W.
ATLANTA, GEORGIA 30315

April 15, 1968

Dear Applicant:

The National Opinion Research Center will be conducting a study (survey) for the Comprehensive Health Program. You have been selected to TRYOUT for a position as an interviewer in the study. Please read the enclosed memo to interviewer applicants. If after you read this memo you would like to tryout for one of twenty positions, call the Comprehensive Health Center at 688-1350 for an appointment.

PLEASE UNDERSTAND THIS IS PART-TIME WORK FOR APPROXIMATELY TWO MONTHS. You will be paid by the hour. The beginning rate will be $1.60 per hour during the training period, and will be increased based on the number of interviews completed.

Thank you for your cooperation.

Sincerely yours,

Geoffrey A. Heard,
Personnel Director

mca
Enclosure

NATIONAL OPINION RESEARCH CENTER
University of Chicago

F-106
4/68

INTERVIEWER APPLICATION

PSU ___________

INT. # ________

1. ▱ Mr. ▱ Mrs. ▱ Miss ____
(First Name) (Middle Initial) (Last Name)

2. Social Security Number ___ - ___ - ______ 3. Date of Birth ___________

4. Street Address ____

5. City ___________________ State _______________ Zip Code ____________

6. Telephone Number: Area Code _________ Home: _________ Other: _________

7. How long have you lived in your community? (CIRCLE ONE NUMBER)

Less than 1 year 1
1 year, less than 3 years . . . 2
3 years, less than 5 years . . 3
5 years or more 4

8. What is your current martial status? (CIRCLE ONE NUMBER)

Married (ANSWER A) 1
Widowed (ANSWER A) 2
Divorced (ANSWER A) 3
Separated (ANSWER A) 4
Never married (GO TO Q. 9) . . . 5

A. IF EVER MARRIED: Do you have to take care of any children under 16 years of age?

Yes (ANSWER B & C) 1
No (GO TO Q. 9) 2

IF YES TO A:

B. How many children? _________

C. What are their ages? ____________________________

9. Enter information for each high school you attended.

Name of School	Location	Years Attended		Diploma Received	
		From	To	Yes	No

10. Enter information for college you attended.

Name of School	Location	Years Attended		If degree, what field?
		From	To	

11. Have you had any other training which you think would be particularly useful to you as an interviewer? If so, describe:

12. Can you speak any languages other than English? (CIRCLE ONE NUMBER)

Yes (ANSWER A & B) 1
No (GO TO Q. 13) 2

IF YES:

A. Which language(s)? (LIST BELOW)	B. Can you interview someone in this language and translate into English at the same time? (CIRCLE ONE NUMBER FOR EACH LANGUAGE LISTED)	
	Yes	No
1		
2		
3		

13. Are you working now? (CIRCLE ONE NUMBER)

Yes (ANSWER A-D) 1
No (GOT TO Q. 14) 2

IF YES:

A. Is this a full-time or part-time job?

Full-time 1
Part-time 2

B. Where are you employed? ______________________

Telephone: ______________________

C. Please describe your work:

D. How long have you been employed there? ______________________

14. PAST EMPLOYMENT RECORD:

Where Employed	Description of Work	Dates Employed		Was that full-time or part-time?	
		From	To	Full	Part

15. Circle each day that you normally CAN WORK on daytime interviewing:

Sun. Mon. Tues. Wed. Thurs. Fri. Sat.

16. Circle each day that you normally CAN WORK on evening interviewing (after 6 P.M.), if necessary:

Sun. Mon. Tues. Wed. Thurs. Fri. Sat.

17. What do you think you would like most about interviewing?

18. What do you think you would like least about interviewing?

19. <u>References</u>: Please give the names of three persons, not relatives, who can tell us most about your qualifications.

Name	Address and City	Position	Employer or Company	How Related to You*

*State whether person is a former or current teacher, an employer or supervisor, or what.

---

20. Who referred you to NORC? ______________________
(Name of person who made referral)

Who is this person? (Give position and agency or organization affiliation.)

____

If no person referred you, please tell how you learned about NORC interviewing.

____

Your Signature ______________

Date of Application ______________

Supervisor's Use: ▱

TQ-8
March, 1968

NATIONAL OPINION RESEARCH CENTER
University of Chicago

SPECIFICATIONS FOR "TRY-OUT" QUESTIONNAIRE

TABLE OF CONTENTS

I. INTRODUCTION

A. The Role of the Research Interviewer

The process of social research involves hundreds of people--the director of a study, his assistants, typists, bookkeepers, data processing technicians, field supervisors, administrative personnel and many others. The work of all these people will be valuable and productive only insofar as you, the research interviewer, perform your task capably and responsibly.

Failure to get accurate responses cannot be remedied in the analysis of the data, no matter how skilled the study director is. Questions omitted by the interviewer represent data permanently lost. Recording meaningful side comments may provide new insights for the study director, as well as furnish him with excellent illustrative material for the final report.

In brief, the interviewer is the eyes and ears of the study director--recording all that is seen and heard. The most brilliant questionnaire design and the most sophisticated analysis of data cannot rescue a study if the interviewing is spotty and inaccurate.

The interviewer, then, is a valuable and crucial link in the long and complex chain of social research.

B. The Ethics of Interviewing

The interviewer in social research must ask many questions he would never dream of asking a close friend, questions one might regard as "too personal." But you will find the average person willing to answer questions--or even volunteering information--he would never tell a close friend or relative. Just as a stranger on a train hears many confidences from people whom he will probably never see again, the interviewer has the great advantage of anonymity which encourages the respondent to confide in him.

The main reason survey research organizations are able to collect useful information is that our interviewers can, and do, assure their respondents that their replies will be completely confidential. We promise the people whom we interview that we will never reveal what they have told us, but simply publish statistics like "17 per cent of the people interviewed think such and such." IT IS YOUR RESPONSIBILITY AS AN INTERVIEWER TO KEEP THAT PROMISE.

The factual material we seek covers some questions that inexperienced interviewers may not like to ask. Again, you need not apologize for asking people's income, whether they voted, their religion and the like. This information, too, is confidential and will never be revealed.

Once in a while a respondent may need reassurance that you're not a welfare investigator, a truant or parole officer, or a bill collector; he may need occasional reminders that the interview is anonymous and that his friends or employer will never know his replies. Never reveal the opinions expressed by anyone you interview. While interviewers are entitled to their own opinions, whatever they are, they cannot let those opinions enter into the interview situation. Moreover they must not report any suspicions which arise as a result of information they get from an interview.

The interviewer has a responsibility here much like that of the clergyman, doctor, or lawyer, none of whom may pass on to others what his clients may have told him in private. The whole basis of opinion research rests on the respondent's confidence that what he says is off the record, and if these confidences were violated the entire profession would suffer great harm.

These rules apply to the opinions you hear, and the information you receive, no matter what the subject. There can be no exceptions to CONFIDENTIALITY.

C. About These Specifications and the Questionnaire

On every NORC study, the interviewer can expect to receive detailed instructions--called Specifications (or "Spex")--on the nature and purpose of the study, the objective of each question, tips on handling the various problems that each question presents, and the deadline for completion and mailing of work. The "Spex" for each study are similar to these, but will include fewer general problems and suggestions than these training specifications.

This is a very special kind of NORC questionnaire. It stresses interviewing problems and techniques. Included are most of the important things that you must learn to be a successful NORC interviewer. While the subject matter of NORC surveys varies, the problems which these questions pose are usually the same problems one faces on any survey. All of the questions in this training questionnaire have been used in previous NORC studies. As it stands, however, this questionnaire is a good deal shorter than those used on most NORC studies.

II. BEGINNING THE INTERVIEW

A. Your Introduction

Introduce yourself in the shortest possible way. Use an introduction something like the one below. Do not let your respondent know that this is a training questionnaire.

> "Hello, I'm Mary Smith. I'm working on a survey of public opinion for the National Opinion Research Center (at the University of Chicago), and we are interested in getting the opinions of people all over the country about the communities in which they live. I'd like to get a few of your ideas."

Try to get inside the house (or apartment) and seated before you really get into the interview. Even though you've seen pictures of "pollsters" standing in the doorway, clipboard in hand, we want you to be inside your respondent's home for the interview. You'll both be more relaxed and more comfortable and so you'll get a better interview. If there seems to be some legitimate reason for not letting you inside don't press the issue, and start your interview at the door. But you'll find yourself seated inside seconds after you have suggested something like: "Why don't we go inside and sit down--I don't want to keep you standing too long!"

Try to interview your respondent alone. The presence of another person may keep the respondent from answering truthfully and fully. It is his opinion we want in this interview, not those of other family members.

B. Answering Some Questions Which You May Be Asked

"How long will it take?"

"That depends on your opinions and how much you have to say. On the average, however, the interview lasts about 20 minutes."

"What is NORC?"

"It's a non-profit research organization. We do these surveys all the time, all over the country." Give the respondent an About NORC folder or a BBB memo. Don't talk about the content of the study--you may bias the respondent's answers.

"What is it about?"

"It is your own opinion about your community. Why don't we start the interview, you'll see."

"Why do you need to know my name?"

"My office needs to know whom I interview." If the respondent objects strenuously, simply record relationships and the other information in Q. 5.

Do not raise any of these questions yourself or offer any of this information unless the respondent asks for it.

III. ASKING THE QUESTIONS

A. General Principles

It is the interviewer's job to make certain that questions are always asked in the same neutral fashion, so that he does not affect the way in which the respondents answer. If each interviewer changed the method of asking questions, we would get interviewer-to-interviewer differences in the responses.

Furthermore, the order in which questions are asked can easily influence the replies. The study director has this in mind when designing the questionnaire, and it is very important that the interviewer follow the order in which the questions are printed.

B. Specific Techniques

To help you follow the general principles for asking questions, these rules should be followed:

1. Ask all questions exactly as they are worded.--If your respondent is talking freely, you may feel that he has already answered some of the questions before you get to them. It is not safe to assume that the respondent has already fully answered a question. Do not skip over any of the questions, even though you guess there may be some repetition. If an occasional respondent should get a little annoyed and say, "I thought I just told you that," you can always say something pleasant like, "Well, the question is down here, and I just wanted to make sure that I had your full answer to that" or "I didn't know whether you would have other things to say on the subject."

2. Ask all questions in the same order as they appear.

3. Make certain that the respondent does not see the questionnaire.--He should not be influenced by knowing what questions are coming.

4. Do not explain words or terms in a question unless the instructions in the Spex for that question tell you to.--Sometimes, respondents will ask you what you mean by certain words, such as "advantage" or "problem" or "danger." Often we are trying to find out exactly how the respondents think of these terms, and therefore we never offer our own explanation. You might reply to a respondent who asks this question by saying, "Whatever you think of as a problem." By this time the respondent will have gained time to collect his thoughts and should be able to answer the question.

In some special situations you may explain a term--in these cases the Spex will tell you what explanation or definition you are authorized to give.

5. Words or phrases in parentheses printed in capital letters are always instructions to interviewers and are not to be read to the respondent.

a. For example, note question 2 in the training questionnaire. The words "HAND CARD A" are not read to the respondent... they are there to remind you to hand the card to the respondent before you ask the rest of the question.

b. Also, in question 1, the word "(CITY)" is an instruction to you to substitute the name of the city in which the respondent lives, when you read the question.

6. All other parenthetical phrases which are not instructions to the interviewer are read at the judgment of the interviewer.--They are in questions for the following purposes.

a. The phrase may be one which will make the wording of the question more appropriate. For example, note Q. 8 in the Training Questionnaire. There we have included the words (husband/wife). You read the word which describes the person about whom you are asking.

b. The phrase may be a suggested probe to get more information from the respondent or to direct his response to the point of the question. For example, note Q. 17A of the Training Questionnaire. The probe "What did he actually do on the job?" is to be used if the respondent gives a vague or general answer at first.

7. Do not read code categories.--As a general rule, the code categories and numbers listed to the right of or below the questions are not read to the respondent. (Sometimes the categories will be included as part of the question itself, and listed below as well; in these cases you read them automatically, because they are part of the question.)

The only exception to this rule is when instructions on the questionnaire or in the specifications tell you to "read the categories."

IV. OBTAINING RESPONSES

A. General Principles

The main task in interviewing is to be sure that you get a statement of your respondent's ideas which is clear and complete. Before you can confidently circle a pre-coded response or leave an open-ended question, you must ask yourself whether the respondent has given a clear answer. Don't accept unclear or vague answers.

An interviewer's performance can be greatly improved if he fully understands the purpose and meaning of each question. Once you know the purpose of a question from the Spex, you will find it much easier to decide if you have a satisfactory answer or whether you should try to get a clearer and fuller one.

In obtaining responses, you must be as neutral as possible. That is, nothing you say or do should affect the way in which the respondent answers a question. The model interviewer is a combination tape recorder and movie camera, simply recording what he hears and sees.

Although the above rule seems sensible and easy to follow, the new interviewer may in practice find it hard not to suggest answers, for in normal conversation we often do so without realizing it. While one may think of interviewing as a friendly conversation, it is actually a rather artificial one.

In most conversations a person who is not certain what his partner means suggests the meaning himself.

Several common ways of carrying on a conversation are not good interviewing techniques because they do suggest answers. Below are some typical problems.

1. Asking whether a person means this or that by a given term suggests one of two answers, even though there may be many other possibilities which the respondent is considering.

Example 1

Question: "In what ways do you feel the public schools in (CITY) could be improved?"

Answer: "The public schools here could be improved by removing some of the people involved."

Incorrect Interviewing Technique: "Do you mean the mayor, or the board of education?" (The respondent may have in mind someone else entirely, or be unclear as to just whom or what he does mean.

Correct Interviewing Technique: "Can you tell me a little more about what you have in mind when you say that?"

2. Trying to summarize what someone has said may suggest to the respondent that your idea of his feelings is the "right answer."

Example 2

Question: "In what ways do you feel the public schools in (CITY) could be improved?"

Answer: "Well, I feel the public schools need a lot of money."

Incorrect Interviewing Technique: "Then you feel they aren't getting enough?" The incorrect probe appears to reword what the respondent said. However, he may have had something else in mind. Perhaps he felt that although the schools need a lot of money, they really were receiving enough already.

Correct Interviewing Technique: "The public schools need a lot of money? What do you mean?"

3. Asking whether he meant a particular thing bv a certain word suggests one answer, when he might have actually meant another one.

Example 3

Question: "What do you think are some of the disadvantages of living in (CITY)?"

Answer:	"The biggest disadvantage for me in living here is the neighborhood."
Incorrect Interviewing Technique:	"By 'neighborhood' do you mean only the neighbors?" The incorrect probe is an attempt to define the term "Neighborhood" for the respondent. Your definition may be quite different than that in the respondent's mind. A neutral probe will give him an opportunity to tell you what he meant.
Correct Interviewing Technique:	"The neighborhood? Tell me a little more about that."

B. Specific Techniques

The general principles in obtaining responses have been presented above. But you must learn certain techniques to be able to do this well. In the paragraphs that follow, then, you will find certain typical situations, with suggestions as to how they should be handled.

1. Open-ended questions

An open-ended question looks like this:

"1. What do you think are some of the advantages in (CITY)?"

Such a question is followed by lots of blank space, with no code number to circle. It's your job to record the respondent's own words--word for word--that is, verbatim, in the space provided. (See Section V-B on pages 11 and 12 for specific techniques in recording and for use of the X probe symbol.)

There are a number of typical interviewing problems caused by respondent's answers--problems which you must solve before you can get a response which will be satisfactory.

The general technique for solving these problems is called "probing" --or continued neutral questioning. It is a procedure which requires sensitivity and skill. Getting full and meaningful responses is perhaps the most challenging part of interviewing--the one thing that requires the most understanding and technique.

The rest of this section presents typical problems, and tips for handling them.

a. Irrelevant answers.--Respondents will sometimes miss the point of the question. Many times they will give responses which at first seem to answer the question but which, you can see when you look further, are not to the point of the question and are therefore irrelevant.

It is easy to be "taken in" by a respondent who is talkative and gives a full and detailed answer--an answer which, however, is quite beside the point. It is not the answer to the question asked.

Interviewers often wonder whether they should actually record the irrelevant response. The answer is "always start recording as the respondent starts talking." If after you start recording you can clearly tell the respondent has missed the point of the question, stop recording and repeat the question, emphasizing those parts of the question which he seems to have missed.

We realize that making the decision as to what is the point, that is, relevant, and what is irrelevant may not always be clear-cut or easy to do in the actual interviewing situation. Therefore, use the following rule of thumb: When you are at all in doubt, write it down. Then probe, by repeating the question or that part of it which the respondent seems to have missed, so that the results will still be a clear and relevant answer.

In most cases, a respondent gives an irrelevant answer because he has missed an important word or phrase in the question. Consider this example:

Q. "What are some of the things you don't like about the way the President is handling our foreign affairs?"

A. "Well, I think he's not trying hard enough to get proper medical care for poor people."

At this point you realize that the respondent is not talking about foreign affairs, so you would probe with:

"I see...but this question deals with foreign affairs. What are some of the things...?"

Emphasizing the word "foreign" will help most respondents to return to the point of the question. Note that this probe is completely neutral: the interviewer does not suggest any of his own ideas.

b. Vague answers.--In everyday social conversation, people normally speak in vague and loose terms. It is understandable that respondents will at first respond to our questions in a manner which is not clear or specific. This is especially true if the questionnaire deals with topics quite distant from the everyday experience or thought of the respondent. It is important to encourage the respondent to express himself more concretely.

Your own probing will be made easier if you assume that each question will be answered in a manner which is vague or general. Thus, you will not have to ask yourself, "Is this a vague response?" but "This is a vague response; how shall I probe?"

Here are some examples of vague answers and suggested probes:

Q. "How would you feel about taking an intelligence test as part of applying for a job?"

A. "I'd like it all right."

PROBE: "Could you explain that a little?"

or:

"You'd like it? How do you mean?"

or:

"Could you tell me more? In what way would you like it?"

Note that the original response is extremely vague. It tells us very little about the respondent's feelings. The question is open-ended (rather than pre-coded) precisely because the study director wants material which is as rich as possible--providing as much detail as the respondent can give. The probes are meant to get the respondent thinking and talking on the subject.

Here again, the neutrality of your probes is important. In no way do the probes shown above suggest to the respondent what the "correct" answer is.

Frequently, the same word used by different respondents will have different meanings, depending on the background of the respondent, where he lives, etc. These, too, should be probed.

For example, a term like "labor" may mean union leaders to one person, but may mean all working men to another.

Descriptive words also mean different things to different people, and unless you probe, the respondent's answer may be lost in the analysis. We all use words which do not have any real content --like "good," "fabulous," "lousy," "wonderful," etc.

Once you train yourself to probe every word of this type, there will be no difficulty in deciding how to probe. You will use probes such as "What do you mean when you say 'good'?" or "Wonderful? In what way?"

c. Don't know.--Respondents might understandably give you a "don't know" to gain some time to gather their thoughts. You've probably noticed your friends--and you yourself--begin answering a question with "I don't know" and then answering it! This might be termed a "lazy don't know" and is simply a way of speaking, to give us time to think of what we have to say. Don't be in too big a rush to settle for a "don't know" reply. If you sit quietly--but expectantly--your respondent will usually think of something further to say. Silence and waiting is frequently your best probe for a "don't know." You'll also find that other useful probes are: "Well, what do you think?" "I just want your own ideas on that." "Nobody really knows, I suppose, but what's your opinion?"

Further, the respondent may feel that there is a right or wrong answer to the question. He may respond with a "don't know" rather than admit his ignorance to what he regards as a factual question.

If you feel this is the case with a respondent, you may reassure him with "There's really no right answer to this question--we're just interested in your opinion." Perhaps you might repeat the question, introducing it with "As you see it..." or "In your opinion..."

d. Circular answers.--Sometimes respondents will answer a question by simply repeating an answer which was already given. A respondent can talk a great deal and still be just repeating the question in different words.

An example:

14. A. How well do you feel tests measure a person's skills and abilities: very well, fairly well, fairly poorly, or very poorly?

Very well . . . 1 51/y
Fairly well . . 2
Fairly poorly . (3)
Very poorly . . 4

B. Why?

"Well, I just don't think they can tell how skillful a person is."

Obviously the answer to the open-ended question (B) will be useless--it tells us absolutely nothing we didn't already know, in the answer to the pre-coded question (A).

Clearly, the most neutral and effective way of probing would be to repeat the question, using the respondent's circular answer, in this manner: "I see, and why do you feel they can't measure a person's skills and abilities?" In this way you are directing his thoughts to the point of the question without adding anything new.

e. Probe for more responses.--Unless instructions on the questionnaire or in the Spex tell you otherwise, always ask for a second response after you have obtained an answer which is relevant and exact. The standard probes here are "What else?" "What other reasons do you have?" "In what other ways do you feel...?"

When such probing is accomplished, the final response you record will usually be something like "None, that's all" or "Nothing else."

However, be sure you have probed to get a clear and complete first answer before trying to get a second one.

This probing for completeness is important because we feel that sometimes the respondent's more deeply felt opinions might be the second or third ones he presents. If we were satisfied with only the first answer to an open-ended question, we would not be getting thorough responses.

To summarize the handling of open-ended questions, your job is to help the respondent give answers which are as relevant, clear, and complete as he is capable of making them.

2. Pre-coded Questions

A "pre-coded" question looks like this:

2. Looking back over the last year or so, would say the world situation is getting better, or getting worse?

Getting better . . 1 6/y
About the same . . 2
Getting worse . . 3
Don't know 4

With this kind of question, you circle the appropriate code number. If the respondent answered "Getting better" to the above, circle the number 1 with a careful circle. If he answered "About the same," then circle 2, and so on. (In circling the code numbers, ignore the number and slash mark to the right of the first "1" in each group of codes. That is the "column number," which tells the office where on an IBM card to punch the code you circled.)

There is much more to a pre-coded question, however, than simply circling a number, as for instance when:

a. The respondent tells more about or explains his choice.

Record (in the blank space to the left of the codes) relevant comments the respondent volunteers as he is answering a pre-coded question. However, do not probe for clarification of these comments.

b. The respondent cannot choose one of the pre-codes given.

It will sometimes happen that the respondent will feel that none of the pre-coded responses fit; or that he would choose one answer under certain conditions, but another answer under different conditions. In this situation you should try to get him to generalize by repeating the question and saying, "Just generally speaking, is it this way or that?" or "Most of the time" or "In most cases," etc. If he insists that he can't choose, you will have to code "don't know." But be sure to record the first response, and your probe mark, before coding the "Don't know."

c. The respondent answers in terms other than the categories included in the questions.

Frequently the respondent will answer using his own words. You may not assume that what he is saying is the same as one of the choices you have read to him. In such an instance repeat the appropriate code categories, saying "Well, would you say ________ or ________ comes closest to your feelings?"

In the situations outlined in b. and c. above, we want you to record verbatim (in the space to the left of the codes) all the respondent's remarks which lead up to his choice of one of the pre-coded responses.

This process will tell us how and why the respondent chose a particular pre-coded response, and will generally tell the study director a great deal about the respondent.

Thus, even in a questionnaire which is heavily pre-coded, we expect to see some verbatim recording. It is an extremely untalkative respondent who doesn't provide you with material for recording in connection with the pre-coded questions.

V. RECORDING RESPONSES

A. General Principles

So far we have reviewed how to ask the questions, and how to get responses. Both of these are very important tasks. Still, if you fail to record the response properly, all your previous efforts will have been wasted.

In general, of course, your recording should reproduce as faithfully as possible what the respondent said. There are a number of specific tips for recording, presented in the next section.

B. Specific Techniques

Word-for-word (verbatim) recording is needed not only on the open-ended questions, but also in the recording which may accompany pre-coded questions. Such recording is difficult, but there are a few ways to help attain this goal:

1. Be ready to write.--Have your pencil poised when you ask your question. Start writing immediately, otherwise you'll be far behind from the beginning.

Soon you'll develop the ability to look at the respondent with an interested expression while recording.

2. Use abbreviations.--However, review the abbreviations you have used during the editing after you return home. If any abbreviations would be confusing to the coders, spell out the term completely while editing. Abbreviations like DK (don't know), gov't., etc., are acceptable.

3. Ask the respondent to slow down.--They're usually flattered when you ask them to speak a little more slowly, or repeat something, or wait a minute until you catch up, because you "don't want to miss anything," or you "want to get this all down." During the early minutes of the interview, you may actually be teaching the respondent how to be a respondent.

4. The X symbol is the probe symbol used by NORC.--Do not write out your probe--simply make an X in your recording at the point you probed. The respondent's answer to your probe would then follow the X.

Perhaps a few words explaining the purpose of probe symbols will make clear for you why it is so important that you use them and use them correctly. We assume that interviewers, after reading these Spex, will use only neutral probes. Therefore, we don't want to know what it is you said (in probing), but we do want to know when you probed. The respondent's answers, mixed in with X's, give us a picture of the conversation which took place. Some respondents answer questions fully and to the point without any encouragement from the interviewer. In such cases we would expect to find fewer probe marks than in cases where getting responses is like pulling teeth. It is important to the study director to know whether the final "I can't think of anything," which the respondent said came after many probes and he really didn't know, or whether it was just a form of a "lazy don't know" which went unprobed. The X probe symbol is your way of telling us that there was some conversation between you and the respondent. Whenever a probe mark "X" is used, some recording should follow. If the respondent says nothing but merely shrugs his shoulders, note this in parentheses following the probe mark.

5. Verbatim recording, of course, means that you should use the respondent's own language word for word.--Don't correct or summarize what he says; let the respondent speak for himself! The study director is as interested in the kinds of words a respondent uses as in the meaning of what he says. The respondent's own words give a good insight into the intensity of his thought.

Be sure to include the pronouns (he, she, it, they)!--Without them the meaning of the response is frequently not so clear as you think.

6. Be sure to use all the white space available.--All four margins, the back of the questionnaire, and blank paper are all available for recording. The more cluttered up the questionnaire, the better!

Also have a blank pad available during the interview for recording answers when the respondent has a lot to say that's to the point and there is not enough space on the questionnaire.

Be sure to identify these loose pieces of paper with the number of the question and place them into the right place in the questionnaire before you return it to our office.

7. Please give your own remarks when you feel something needs explaining.--But be sure to put them in parentheses, so we don't confuse your explanation with the response. You might want to make explanations like (respondent began fidgeting), (baby starts crying), (respondent laughed), etc.

8. On pre-coded questions, carefully circle only one code (unless the question calls for circling more than one).--It is unfortunate to

have to throw out an answer because the interviewer, in a hurry, made a large circle which covered two codes, so we didn't know which was meant.

9. If it is necessary to change a code, be sure to tell us the reason.--That is--if the respondent changes his mind after you have already circled one code, cross out the wrong code and note next to it (in parentheses) "R changed mind." If you circled the wrong code by mistake, cross it out, and note--again in parentheses--"my error" (M.E.).

10. Of course, readable handwriting is important, but we want you to be more concerned about getting full, rich material during the interview. You can make words more readable later, when you're editing the questionnaire.

VI. EDITING THE INTERVIEW

Take a few minutes right after you complete each interview to inspect the questionnaire and make sure it is all filled out accurately and completely. Do this before you go on to conduct the next interview. This procedure is known as editing, and, though it doesn't take long, it is an important part of an interviewer's job. Some of the purposes of editing are:

A. To Catch, and Correct or Explain, Errors and Omissions in Recording

Common errors that can be caught in editing are: omitted codes, unnecessary questions asked, and errors in circling codes. In the pressure of the interview situation the interviewer may make any of these errors; most of them could be corrected by the interviewer if she edits carefully immediately after the interview.

B. To Learn from Mistakes So They Are Not Repeated

C. To Clarify Handwriting and Write Out Abbreviations That Are Not Commonly Used

D. To Add Your Comments in Parentheses Which Might Help Us To Understand a Response or an Interview as a Whole

VII. QUESTION-BY-QUESTION SPECIFICATIONS

Introduction: Use the introduction given at the beginning of the questionnaire, and fill in your own name.

Time Began: As you are about to begin the interview, record the time.

Q. 1: If a range of years is mentioned that falls between two categories ("about five to seven years"), then try to narrow down the response. Probe: "Would you say it is closer to five years or closer to seven years?" If the respondent doesn't remember the exact time, then ask for his best guess.

Q. 2: Card A is used with this question. Hand it to the respondent so he can choose one of the four categories for each service you mention. Be sure to circle one and only one code number in each row. If the respondent asks you what you mean by "community," tell him "whatever you think of as your community."

Start reading the question with "First how about schools...would you say you are very satisfied, somewhat satisfied, somewhat dissatisfied or very dissatisfied?" Code the response to that, then ask about item B--"Police protection" and continue through the list until it is complete.

Although the respondent may feel he doesn't know about some of these services, try to get him to tell you how he feels by saying, "just your impression from what you have heard or read." If he simply cannot choose, after you have probed, circle the "Don't know" code.

Q's. 3 and 4: These two "school" questions can be thought of as a unit since they are identical with one exception. Q. 3 discusses elementary school, which is defined as kindergarten through 8th grade, and Q. 4 discusses high school, which is defined as grades 9 through 12. If there are children attending junior high school, determine which grade and enter in either Q. 3 or Q. 4, according to the above definition.

This is a good place to introduce and explain the term "skip directions." It applies to the instructions printed in capital letters that tell you which questions or parts of questions to ask next. These skip directions are used when the next question (or series of questions) to be asked depends on the answer you have just received. These directions are printed in capital letters and are not to be read to the respondent.

For example, look at the skip pattern in Q. 3. The skip directions tell you that if the answer to the main question is "no children in elementary school," you circle code 2 and go on to Q. 4. If the answer is "yes," you find out how many by asking "A" and, if more than one, if they attend the same schools. Then you ask "B," using the appropriate wording--"Is that a..." if only one child, or two or more children attend the same school; "Are they..." if more than one child and they attend different schools. The same skip pattern is used in Q. 4.

Q. 5A: At this point in the interview we do a household enumeration, which is a list of all persons living in the household and certain information about each person. Record the respondent's name on the first line of the boxes, under "A."

A person is considered to be living in the household if:

(a) This is his regular home, or

(b) He or she is staying here at the time of your call and has no regular home elsewhere (for example, a woman who takes turns living in the households of her children).

Do not consider as living in the household any member of the family who lives elsewhere, even though the family "saves a room" for him or her. For example:

A person who is in a mental institution or other institution at the time you call.

A man in the armed forces who is living at his army quarters where he regularly sleeps.

However, someone who is in the hospital temporarily, but expects to return to this address should be listed. A traveling salesman or husband who works in another city or who travels from place to place is also considered as living with the family if he regularly returns home.

Record FIRST and LAST names for all persons listed. DO NOT ASSUME THAT ALL HOUSEHOLD MEMBERS HAVE THE SAME LAST NAME.

"B," "C," "D": Record the relationship to the respondent, the age on the last birthday, and the sex of each person. Frequently the respondent will tell you the relationships as he or she tells you the names of the people. Be careful to record the relationship to the respondent.

"E": Be sure to ask about the marital status for each person who is 14 years or older.

"F": For the purpose of this questionnaire, the "head of the household" is anyone who is considered the "head" by the respondent. Some people consider the person who earns the most money as the "head," others consider the oldest person as the "head," while others will consider the husband as the "head," whether or not he is the oldest or the main provider.

If two or more unrelated people live together (e.g., roommates), and they are equally the "head," consider your respondent as the head of the household.

Q. 6: Be sure to read the short introduction above the question. This helps the respondent start thinking about the subject that's coming. Note that the code categories are in the question itself. The "don't know" category is not listed in the question--it is never mentioned to the respondent. Be sure to ask "B" if the respondent has mentioned a spouse in the enumeration. Read the correct word "husband" or "wife" depending on which one you are talking about.

Note that the question is put in terms of the person's usual health. Therefore, if the respondent says, "Well, I've got a bad cold today, so I'd say poor," record this verbatim and repeat the question, to ask him about his health in general.

Q. 7A: If the respondent volunteers that he went to a doctor when something was bothering him, repeat the question, stressing the words, "when you were feeling all right?"

Q. 7A(1): You will notice that the categories below this question are not included in the question itself. This means that you do not read the code categories.

Q. 7B(2) will probably have to be probed, to find out how or why the things mentioned kept the person from seeing a doctor. Write down whatever the respondent says in reply to your question, but then be sure to probe if his answer is vague or irrelevant. Here are some examples:

Vague Answers:

If the respondent mentions, "The amount of pain that I had," or "The children," or "I got scared," you would record it verbatim and probe with "Why did that keep you from going to the doctor--can you tell me a little more about that?"

Answers like "Money" or "No time" should be probed with: "Money...in what way?" or "What do you have in mind when you say no time?" One-word answers to an open-ended question should always be probed. There may be times when you may think you know what the respondent means by a one-word reply, but you can't be sure unless you ask, and you must still probe so we know exactly what the respondent had in mind.

Sometimes the respondent will mention many reasons very quickly. Write them all down, and then go back and ask about each one that is unclear. You might say, "Now you just mentioned...it's inconvenient...in what way is it inconvenient?" When this idea is clear, you should continue to probe the next reason mentioned, until you have clarified each reason mentioned.

Irrelevant Answers: An answer like, "Well, I didn't go but I thought I should go because..." doesn't answer the question if the respondent goes on to tell you why she thought she should go. Bring her back to the point of the question by saying, "Well, what were some of the things that kept you from going?"

Complete Answers: Here we want all of the things that kept the respondent from going to the doctor. First, probe each reason the respondent mentions to be sure it is clear, then probe, "What other things kept you from going to the doctor?" Continue using this probe until the respondent tells you, "I can't think of any others" or "That's all."

Q's. 8, 9 and 10: Ask Q. 8 first for the respondent and then for the husband or wife (if there is one) before going on to Q. 9. Then ask Q. 9 for both before going on to Q. 10.

Q. 8 refers to conditions that people usually have for long periods of time. Some other examples of such conditions are asthma or allergies. The person himself need not have had the condition for a long time. If he says, "I just developed high blood pressure recently," code "yes."

Q. 9 refers to all other illnesses not mentioned in Q. 8.

Q. 10 is asked to pick up any illnesses we might have missed.

Q. 11: Check your answers to Q's. 8, 9 and 10 for the respondent. If you have coded a "yes" to one or more of these questions about the respondent, ask Q. 11 for him or her. Then do the same for the spouse. If there are no "yeses" to Q's 8, 9 or 10 for either the respondent or the spouse, skip to Q. 12.

Q. 13A: If the respondent asks--by "Bed patient" we mean "Not the emergency room or the out-patient clinic, but a bed inside the hospital."

If the respondent gives a "don't know" answer to Part A, probe by explaining that he need not have any first-hand experience, that you just want his preference . . . "on the basis of whatever you've heard or read." If he still says he doesn't know, circle code 1 and go on to Q. 14. Of course, you will record his remarks verbatim.

If the respondent names two or more hospitals as his choice, probe for the one he would most likely choose.

A respondent may sometimes have a particular hospital in mind, but may not know its exact name. In such cases, probe for the location of the hospital, as exactly as the respondent can give it to you, so that we can properly classify the answer. For example, the respondent may tell you "Medical Center" or "St. John's," or "the Professional Hospital." Since there are many hospitals using these names, you must get a more complete title, such as "University Medical Center" or "St. John's Episcopal Hospital on Herkimer Street."

Q. 13B: Follow the procedures described earlier for getting as full, clear answers as you can to this open-ended question.

Q's. 14 and 15: Never be apologetic about seeking this kind of information. Asking factual questions about the respondent himself is standard practice for social surveys, and the results of an interview are worthless without these data. If you make excuses or appear uncomfortable, the person is likely to think you have an ulterior motive for seeking such information about him. But if you ask the questions in a business-like manner and in a matter-of-fact tone of voice, the respondent will answer them in the same way.

Don't be surprised, however, if some persons, before they answer, want to know why you want such information. A great majority of the curious can be satisfied by the simple reply: "We need this information for statistical purposes only." To the more persistent, you may go on to explain that we have to be sure we're interviewing the proper number of people in different occupations, age groups, nationalities, etc.--in order to make certain that our survey is accurate, and that it fairly represents all kinds of people.

Q's. 14 and 15 are to be asked about the Head of the household. (Check back to the enumeration to see who the Head is.) If your respondent is another member of the household, use the other version, in which you insert the name (or relationship to respondent) of the Head. That is, you could either say, "Mr. Smith" or "Your husband."

Hand the respondent Card B as you ask Q. 14. If he has difficulty reading the categories, you may read them aloud to him. Note that if the Head is keeping house, in school, or "other" you ask sub-question A.

The "other" category includes anything that doesn't fit the categories provided.

Q. 15A: The occupation or "kind of work done" question requests exactly the information that you think it does--a description of the duties performed by the head on his job. A brief description is not a good one if it does not give you a picture of what he actually does. Your job is to encourage the respondent to spell out the duties. Consider the following examples:

(1) Occasionally the occupation will be reported "farmer." Granted that we know that he works with soil and seed, the answer is still incomplete because he could

a) own a farm
b) rent a farm
c) be a sharecropper
d) work without pay on his family's farm
e) be a farm laborer, or
f) be a foreman on a farm.

In this type of case, we must know which of these possibilites apply to the person in question.

(2) Another tricky situation arises when a person reports the Head is a "laborer." The answer is not enough. The Bureau of the Census lists 91 different types of laborers and we simply must know what this person's "labors" are if we are going to be able to classify him. "What sort of things (do you/does he) do as a laborer?" is a useful probe, and it is not hard to think of others.

The same guidelines apply to responses like "factory work," "work on an assembly line," "office work," "sales work," "repairman," "painter," "engineer," "clerical," and many other answers you will get.

Q. 15B: It is also important that we have detailed information about the type of business or industry in which the Head is employed--not only what they make or do (the end product), but also what they have to do with that product.

Consider the following descriptions--all of which are not satisfactory:

a) "A private firm"--What kind of business does the firm engage in?

b) "Government service"--Is that national, state, county or city goverment?

c) "Henry Mills and Sons" (Apparently Mrs. Mills has brought his sons into the business but what kind of business are they in?)

d) "Automobiles"--This could refer to an auto factory, a retail automobile dealer, or something else.

e) "Hardware"--Does this refer to a factory which produces hardware items, a wholesale hardware distributor, or neighborhood hardware store?

Probe fully. Break these answers down and spell out exactly what kind of business or industry the Head is in.

Of course, we are aware that you may not be able to get complete and detailed answers from all of your respondents--especially when you are asking a respondent about someone else's occupation. However, you are expected to know the kind and extent of information to probe for. You should never accept a partial, incomplete, or vague answer without probing for more detail. If you then get a "don't know," you have done your best, and that is what we are asking. Respondents really don't mind answering these questions, so you needn't feel hesitant about asking them.

Q. 16: "Highest grade completed" refers to years of formal schooling. Count correspondence and vocational training only if they represent work toward a regular diploma or degree.

Be sure to ask for and code all three parts--A, B, and C.

You may have to encourage a respondent to "guess" about his parents' schooling. Some will have only a vague idea. Get their best estimate. If your respondent or either of his parents was educated in a foreign country record the situation verbatim and ask the respondent which code category would be closest to our grade, then code accordingly.

Q. 17: Our earlier instructions concerning occupation and industry also apply here. Another phrasing is provided in the questionnaire for persons without fathers at age 16.

Q. 18: "Religion" does not mean that the person needs to belong to a church--just what he thinks of as his religion.

Q. 19: Remember to ask sub-question A if you circle code 2 for the main question.

Q. 20: Hand the respondent Card C when asking the question. If the respondent says "Don't know" or refuses to answer, circle the appropriate code, either "Y" or "Z," and give us your best guess of the family's income by writing down the appropriate code number in the space provided.

Q. 21: If the respondent says he has no phone number, be sure to circle "1" for "no phone." This is the last question you ask the respondent.

ITEMS TO BE FILLED OUT AFTER LEAVING THE RESPONDENT:

Remember to record the time the interview ended, and the total length of time the interview took. Do not count interruptions of more than ten minutes when you total the length of interview. Then fill in items B through E immediately.

TQ-8
March, 1968

NATIONAL OPINION RESEARCH CENTER
University of Chicago

"TRY-OUT" QUESTIONNAIRE

A questionnaire to be used by applicants to conduct an interview as part of the hiring process.

INTRODUCTION AT DWELLING UNIT:

Hello, I'm ______ from the National Opinion Research Center. We are interested in getting the opinion of people all over the country about the communities in which they live.

ENTER TIME INTERVIEW BEGAN: ________A.M. ________P.M

---

1. How long you have lived in (CITY)?

Less than 4 years	1
4 yrs. but less than 6 . . .	2
6 yrs. but less 10	3
10 years or more	4

---

2. Would you please tell me how satisfied you are with the way various services are provided in this community --

First, how about schools -- Would you say you are very satisfied, somewhat satisfied, somewhat dissatisfied, or very dissatisfied? (REPEAT FOR ITEMS B-F.)

	Very Satisfied	Somewhat Satisfied	Somewhat Dissatisfied	Very Dissatisfied	Don't Know
A. Schools?	1	2	3	4	5
B. Police protection? . .	6	7	8	9	0
C. Job training--that is, places where adults can attend classes or can receive instruction in various subjects?	1	2	3	4	5
D. Street lighting? . . .	6	7	8	9	0
E. Hospital facilities? .	1	2	3	4	5
F. Public transportation?	6	7	8	9	0

3. Do you have any children in elementary or grade schools?

Yes . (ASK A & B) 1
No . (GO TO Q. 4) 2

IF YES, ASK A & B:

A. How many children?

One child . (GO TO B) 1
More than one (RECORD NUMBER: ______
AND ASK [1])

IF MORE THAN ONE: [1] Do they all attend the same elementary school?

Yes . (ASK B) 1
No . (ASK B) 2

B. (Is that a)(Are they) public or private schools(s)?

Public school only 1
Private school only 2
Public & private schools . . 3

---

4. Do you have any children in high school?

Yes . (ASK A & B) 1
No . (GO TO Q. 5) 2

IF YES, ASK A & B:

A. How many children?

One child . (GO TO B) 1
More than one (RECORD NUMBER: ______
AND ASK [1])

IF MORE THAN ONE: [1] Do they all attend the same high school?

Yes . (ASK B) 1
No . (ASK B) 2

B. (Is that a)(Are they) public or private high school(s)?

Public high school only . . . 1
Private high school only . . 2
Public and private high
schools 3

5. Now I'd like to list the people who live here. (ENTER RESPONDENT'S FULL NAME ON FIRST LINE.)

   A. Who else lives here? (ENTER NAMES OF SPOUSE, CHILDREN, THEN ANY OTHER PEOPLE ON SUCCEEDING LINES.)

      (1) Have we missed anyone, such as small children or babies? (ENTER NAMES BELOW.)

      (2) Are there any others who usually live here, but who are away from home now--traveling, in a hospital, on vacation, or at school, or somewhere else? (ENTER NAMES BELOW.)

   RECORD IN APPROPRIATE COLUMN THE FOLLOWING FOR EACH PERSON LISTED.

   B. What is (PERSON'S) relationship to you?

   C. What was (PERSON'S) age on (his/her) last birthday?

   D. RECORD SEX.

   E. FOR EACH PERSON 14 YEARS OR OLDER, ASK: Is (PERSON) married, single, widowed, or divorced?

   F. Who is the head of the household? (CHECK APPROPRIATE BOX.)

A. PRINT NAMES First Last	B. RELATIONSHIP TO RESPONDENT	C. AGE	D. SEX	E. MARITAL STATUS	F. HEAD
	Respondent				

Now I have some questions about health.

6. A. Would you say your own health, in general, is excellent, good, fair, or poor?

Excellent 1
Good 2
Fair 3
Poor 4
Don't know 5

B. IF MARRIED: How about the health of your (husband/wife) -- In general, would you rate it as excellent, good, fair, or poor?

Excellent 6
Good 7
Fair 8
Poor 9
Don't know 0

---

7. We're interested in how people feel about getting physical check-ups --

A. Have you ever gone for a medical examination when you were feeling all right?

Yes . (ASK [1] THEN GO TO B) . . 1
No . (GO TO B) 2

IF YES: [1] When was the last time that you did this? (PROBE FOR BEST GUESS.)

6 months ago or less 1
7 months, less than 1 year . . . 2
1 year, less than 2 years 3
2 years ago or more 4
Don't know 5

B. Have there been times when you didn't go to see a doctor, even though you thought you should?

Yes . (ASK [2]) 1
No . (GO TO Q. 8) 2

IF YES TO B: [2] What are some of the things that kept you from going to the doctor?

ASK EACH QUESTION FOR RESPONDENT AND SPOUSE(IF ANY) BEFORE GOING ON TO NEXT QUESTION	1 2 3 4 5 6 7	1 2 3 4 5 6 7
8. Did you (your husband/wife) see a doctor during the last 12 months for any kind of illness that people have for a long time, such as high blood pressure, heart condition, arthritis, diabetes, or anything else like that?	(Respondent) Yes (ASK A) . . 1 No . . . . 2 DK 3	(Spouse) Yes (ASK A) . . 1 No . . . . 2 DK 3
IF YES, ASK A A. What was the condition?	A.__________	A.__________
9. Did you (your husband/wife) see a doctor during the same 12 months for any (other) kind of illness, or any injury or accident?	Yes (ASK A) . . 1 No . . . . 2 DK 3	Yes (ASK A) . . 1 No . . . . 2 DK 3
IF YES, ASK A A. What was the condition?	A.__________	A.__________
10. Did you (your husband/wife) see a doctor in those 12 months for any reason we haven't already talked about -- such as a cold, indigestion, or any other things?	Yes (ASK A) . . 1 No . . . . 2 DK 3	Yes (ASK A) . . 1 No . . . . 2 DK 3
IF YES, ASK A A. What was the condition?	A.__________	A.__________
ASK Q. 11 FOR EACH PERSON WHO ANSWERED YES TO Q. 8 OR 9 OR 10. IF THERE ARE NO CODES CIRCLED "YES," SKIP TO Q. 12.		
11. Where did you (your husband/wife) get your (his/her) medical care the last time -- from a private doctor, a hospital clinic, emergency room, or some other place?	Private doctor 1 Hospital clinic 2 Emergency room 3 Other (SPECIFY) 4	Private doctor 1 Hospital clinic 2 Emergency room 3 Other (SPECIFY) 4

12. Do you think the average person can tell whether a doctor is well qualified, or do you think it takes an expert to know this?

Average person 1

Takes an expert 2

Don't know 3

---

13. A. If you had to go to the hospital as a bed patient, which hospital would you choose -- if you could go wherever you liked? (PLEASE PRINT NAME.)

Don't know (GO TO Q. 14) . . 1

B. Why would you choose that one? (PROBE: What other reasons would you have for going to that one?

ASK Q'S. 14 & 15 ABOUT HEAD OF HOUSEHOLD.

14. HAND CARD B — Which of the activities on this card covers what (you were/HEAD was) doing last week?

Working full time (35 hours or more) (GO TO Q. 15) . . . 1

Working part time (GO TO Q. 15) 2

Has a job, but not at work because of temporary illness, vacation, strike, weather conditions, or personal reasons (GO TO Q. 15) 3

Unemployed and looking for work, or laid off (GO TO Q. 15) 4

Retired (ASK Q. 15) 5

Keeping house (ASK A) 6

In school (ASK A) 7

Other (SPECIFY AND ASK A) 8

IF KEEPING HOUSE, IN SCHOOL OR OTHER, ASK A:

A. Did (you/HEAD) ever work for as long as one year?

Yes (GO TO Q. 15) 1

No (SKIP TO Q. 16) 2

---

15. A. What kind of work (do you/does HEAD) (did you/did HEAD) normally do?

OCCUPATION: ______________________________

(IF VAGUE, PROBE: What (do/does/did) (you/HEAD) actually do on this job?)

B. In what kind of business or industry (is/was) that?

BUSINESS OR INDUSTRY: ______________________________

(IF VAGUE, PROBE: What does that (firm/organization/agency) make or do?)

16.

	A. What was the highest grade you completed in school?	B. What was the highest grade your father completed?	C. What was the highest grade your mother completed?
GRADE SCHOOL	00	00	00
	01	01	01
	02	02	02
	03	03	03
	04	04	04
	05	05	05
	06	06	06
	07	07	07
	08	08	08
HIGH SCHOOL	09	09	09
	10	10	10
	11	11	11
	12	12	12
COLLEGE	13	13	13
	14	14	14
	15	15	15
	16	16	16
GRADUATE OR PROFESSIONAL	17+	17+	17+
Don't know	XX	XX	XX

17. A. What kind of work did your father do when you were about 16 years old? (IF NOT LIVING WITH FATHER AT THAT TIME, ASK: Well, what about the person who contributed the most to your support in those days?)

KIND OF WORK: ____
(PROBE: What did he actually do on that job?)

B. In what kind of business or industry did he work?

BUSINESS OR INDUSTRY: ________________________________
(PROBE: What did that (firm/organization/agency) make or do?)

18. What is your religion?

Protestant (ASK A) 1
Catholic 2
Jewish 3
None 4
Other (SPECIFY) 5

IF PROTESTANT: A. What denomination? ____________________

---

19. Did you vote in the last Presidential election?

Yes 1
No (ASK A) 2

IF NO, ASK: A. Were you registered to vote?

Yes 1
No 2

---

20. Now to finish up -- in which of these general groups did your total family income fall last year, before taxes, that is?

HAND CARD C

A. Under $1,000 X
B. $1,000 - 1,999 0
C. $2,000 - 2,999 1
D. $3,000 - 3,999 2
E. $4,000 - 4,999 3
F. $5,000 - 5,999 4
G. $6,000 - 6,999 5
H. $7,000 - 7,999 6
I. $8,000 - 9,999 7
J. $10,000 - 14,999 8
K. $15,000 or more 9
Don't know . . . . y*
Refused . . . . z*

*INTERVIEWER ESTIMATE:
Category ________

---

21. Finally, may I have your telephone number, in case my office wants to verify this interview?

Telephone No.: ____________________ Area Code: __________

No phone 1

IMPORTANT -- FILL IN THE ITEMS BELOW IMMEDIATELY AFTER LEAVING RESPONDENT.

TIME ENDED:__________A.M.
__________P.M.

Total length of interview:__________minutes

A. Respondent's Name: ______________________________

Address: ______________________________

City & State: ______________________________

B. Respondent's race:

White 1
Negro 2
Other (SPECIFY) 3

C. Interest of respondent:

Very interested 1
Somewhat interested 2
Uninterested 3

D. Date of interview:

____

E. Interviewer's signature:

____

APPLICANT CARD

APPT: ________

RECRUITMENT FILE CARD

NAME: ________

ADDRESS: ________ REF. BY: ________

PHONE: ________ Age: ________ EDUCATION: ________

Date Application Received: ________ Emp. ________ Unemp. ________

Date	Personal Interview Rating	POSITIVE FACTORS: NEGATIVE FACTORS:

Date to Return Second Screener: ________ Time: ________

Date	Screener Received Rating	UNDERSTANDING OF SPEX: PRECODED: OPEN END:

HIRED ________
NOT HIRED ________
Lister ________

COMMENTS:

SRS-4053

DAILY CHECK-IN SHEET

DATE	APPLICATION NUMBER	SCREENERS GIVEN	PERSONAL INTERVIEW RATING	SCREENER RATING

SRS-4053
Recruiting
________(P.I.R.)

PROGRESS REPORT

DATE	TOTAL SEEN	TQ GIVEN						
			A	B	C	D	UNRATED	TOTAL RECD.

ACCEPTANCE LETTER

COMPREHENSIVE HEALTH CENTER
1070 WASHINGTON STREET, S. W.
ATLANTA, GEORGIA 30315

We are very pleased to let you know that you have been selected for the Comprehensive Health Center Survey.

Your beginning rate will be $1.75 per hour, plus expenses (such as carfare).

Training classes will begin:

Day: ____________________

Date: ____________________

Hour: ____________________

Place: 1070 Washington Street, S. W.

We look forward to seeing you on time. If for any reason you are no longer interested in the job, please call Mrs. Calloway, 688-1350, so another applicant can be selected.

Sincerely yours,

(Mrs.) Fan Calloway, Field Director
National Opinion Research Center

FC/lgb

REJECTION LETTER

COMPREHENSIVE HEALTH CENTER
1070 WASHINGTON STREET, S. W.
ATLANTA, GEORGIA 30315

Thank you very much for your interest in applying for the job as interviewer for the Comprehensive Health Center Survey. As you know, more than one hundred people applied, and from this group we could select only 25-30 persons.

We are very sorry that we cannot hire you at this time, but if any openings occur at a later date, we will reconsider those persons who were not selected in the first group.

There are other job openings at the Center for which you will be considered as soon as these positions become available.

Sincerely yours,

(Mrs.) Fan Calloway, Field Director
National Opinion Research Center

FC/lgb

ARITHMETIC QUIZ

The following test was developed and used for the first time in connection with the health center study in Charleston, South Carolina. It is particularly useful in giving additional relevant arithmetic training to interviewers who may require it.

1. Mr. Brown gets paid $95.00 every two weeks. How much does he earn per week?

   How much does he earn per month?

   How much per year?

2. Sallie makes $1.75 per hour. She works 7½ hours each day. She works Monday through Friday. How many hours does she work each week? How much does she earn per week; how much per year?

3. Atty. Jones makes $18,000 per year. How much does he earn per month?

4. If you received $85.00 per week in salary, how much would that be per year? How much per month?

5. John's salary is $32.75 per day as an official at Kerrison's. How much does he make per week? He works 6½ days each week.

6. If an interview begins at 9:15 in the morning and ends at 11:45 a.m., how much time has elapsed?

7. You work from 11:30 a.m. until 4:15 p.m., how many hours have you worked? How many minutes have you worked?

8. You come into the office at 10:40 and leave at 12:00 noon. How long were you here?

9. Your interview with six people in the family began at 1:15 p.m. and ended at 4:30 p.m. How long did it take?

10. If the Brown family earned the following amounts each week, how much is their total weekly income?

John Brown	$52.80
Mary Brown	39.46
Susie Brown	36.65
Robert Brown	69.00

    How much do they earn per month; per year?

APPENDIX B

ADMINISTRATIVE MATERIALS

LIST OF FURNITURE AND SUPPLIES

Furniture and supplies required to run a survey field office for survey yielding approximately 1,500 cases.

3	desks with desk chairs (one of these should be for a secretary)
1	typewriter and stand
2-3	waste baskets
1	four-drawer file cabinet (or equivalent)
24 ft.	of shelf space (could be two units of four by three shelves each)
6	eight-foot folding tables
40-50	chairs (preferably folding chairs)
2	blackboards (with chalk and erasers)
1 or 2	coat rack(s)
1	pencil sharpener
200	pencils (with erasers)
75	pads of lined paper
1	box typing bond

Before the recruitment of interviewers can begin, the above should be available in the survey office.

NORC
4052

FOR OFFICE USE ONLY:

No. Interviews Rec'd ________

Checked by ________

INTERVIEWER'S TIME REPORT

DAY ____________ DATE ____________

Mr., Mrs., or Miss ______________________

Street Address ______________________

City, State, Zip Code ______________________

____
Signature of Interviewer

CLOCK TIME			ELAPSED TIME		Travel	Inter-viewing	Other Time	Explain "Other Time"	COMPLETED CASES		EXPENSES	
From	To		Hrs	Min					Seg. #	Line #	Explain	Amount
		=										$
		=										
		=										
		=										
Total Hours									Total No. Cases		Total Amount	$

FOR OFFICE USE ONLY: Total Hours ______ X ______ Rate = ______ Salary + ______ Expense = ______ Pay

INTERVIEWER IDENTIFICATION CARDS

---

is a qualified interviewer for the

NATIONAL OPINION RESEARCH CENTER

A non-profit organization affiliated with the

UNIVERSITY OF CHICAGO

6030 South Ellis Avenue

Chicago, Illinois 60637

NORMAN M. BRADBURN, *Director*

This identification is valid for the calendar year__________

SIGNATURE OF INTERVIEWER

This is to certify that

---

is a qualified interviewer for the

COMPREHENSIVE HEALTH CENTER HEALTH SURVEY
1070 Washington Street, S.W.
Atlanta, Georgia 30315

Co-directors:

Calvin A. Brown, Jr., M.D.

William M. Marine, M.D.

Signature of Interviewer

APPENDIX C

SAMPLING MATERIALS

Page / of ___ Pages

DWELLING UNIT LISTING SHEET (DULS)

NORC
F-78A
4/68

Segment No.__________

City__________________________ Census Tract__________ Block(s)__________

DIAGRAM OF SEGMENT

(Start at the "X" and follow the arrows which show the direction for listing.)

(Fill this in after completing the listing.)
Lister's Name______________________________
Date______________ Total DU's______

List every DU located within this segment. Start at the "X" and go in order around the segment. Go in and out of each street, alley, or road within the segment as you come to it. Continue until you have reached your starting point again. Use one line for each DU.

N
W E
S

BE SURE THAT EVERY PLACE OF RESIDENCE IS LISTED AND THAT ALL APARTMENTS, ETC., ARE NUMBERED OR OTHERWISE IDENTIFIED SO THAT SOMEONE ELSE COULD FIND THIS PARTICULAR DU.

Line No.	NAME AND ADDRESS OR DESCRIPTION OF DWELLING UNIT Indicate house number and street name. Identify apartments by floor, number, and location. If this is not possible, describe dwelling unit and its location in detail. Also enter the name of the resident of those DU's for which there are no apartment numbers.		Negro or White	Language	Assignment Line
	Street Address	Apt. No. or Name, if necessary			
1					
2					
3					
4					
5					
6					
7					
8					
9					

(OVER)

Page 2 of ___ Pages

LISTING CONTINUATION SHEET

NORC
F-78A
4/68

Segment No.___________

Line No.	NAME AND ADDRESS OR DESCRIPTION OF DWELLING UNIT Indicate house number and street name. Identify apartments by floor, number, and location. If this is not possible, describe dwelling unit and its location in detail. Also enter the name of the resident of those DU's for which there are no apartment numbers.		Negro or White	Language	Assignment Line
	Street Address	Apt. No. or Name, if necessary			
10					
11					
12					
13					
14					
15					
16					
17					
18					
19					
20					
21					
22					
23					
24					
25					

(Use a continuation sheet, if necessary)

NORC
4052
(Rev. 7-68)

HOW TO LIST FOR AN AREA SAMPLE

Table of Contents

I. Why Must We List?

In order to interview the people of a particular area, we must first find some way of drawing up a list and from that list pick up every 10th or 100th person (or whatever number we decide depending on how many cases are needed), in order to find out something about all the people who live in this area. Since no lists of all the people are available, and yet everyone in the area must be given an equal chance of being picked for an interview, we LIST all the DWELLING UNITS in the area and then pick our 10th or 100th (or whatever number) dwelling unit. The people who happen to live in that dwelling unit then become eligible to be interviewed.

It is your job to provide us with this listing of dwelling units and to do it as accurately as possible, so that when the results of the study are in, we can be sure that everyone in the area is truly represented.

II. How To Use the Maps

A segment usually consists of a block or part of a block, or it may even be an area consisting of several blocks. The Dwelling Unit Listing Sheet for each segment gives a sketch of the bloc (or blocks), showing the names of the streets or other boundaries within which all dwelling units are to be listed for that segment. Note the street names, or names of other boundary lines, such as roads, expressways, railroad lines, etc.

A. Finding the Segments. A city street map will help you find the general location of the segment and the best way to get to it. When you get there, use both the map and the sketch on the Dwelling Unit Listing Sheet to find the exact boundaries of the segment in which you are to list. These boundaries are usually streets, but they may also be railroads, subway lines, or highways. Sometimes street names of one or more of the segment boundaries did not exist at the time the map was drawn (as, for example, in new housing developments), or may not have been known to the person who made the segment sketch. In this case, the general shape of the segment and those boundaries which are given will guide you in knowing whether or not you are in the right block. You must always take a walk around the block before you start any work on the listings and make sure you have the right block. All the boundaries must agree. For example, if the block is square the names of three boundaries could agree and you could be on the wrong block--you could be in the neighboring block.

B. If You Cannot Locate the Segment. If, when you get to the area, you cannot locate the exact segment because a street name or other boundary information has been changed recently, make a note to yourself of where our information differs from what you actually find, and call your supervisor. But be sure you can tell her exactly which street name should be on the map instead of the one we have indicated.

III. How To List Dwelling Units

A. List All Dwelling Units on the "Dwelling Unit Listing Sheet" (DULS)

Once you are sure that you are in the right segment and know its boundaries, list one dwelling unit on each line of the DULS until you have listed every dwelling unit in the segment. DO NOT SKIP ANY LINES. Use front and back of the DULS before going on to the next, or a Continuation Sheet. Make sure each sheet is numbered (that is, sheet 2, sheet 3, etc.). Later you will write on each sheet used, in a segment, the total number of sheets in the set needed for that segment (for example, sheet 1 of a total of 3 sheets, sheet 2 of a total of 3 sheets, etc.). See examples at the end of these instructions.

B. Eleven Rules To Follow for Accurate Listing

RULE I — List all dwelling units. Be sure you account for all dwelling units in every residential building.

a. What is a "Dwelling Unit"? (According to the U. S. Census Bureau) A room or group of rooms is a dwelling unit when it is used or intended to be used as separate living quarters. Living quarters are separate when:

(1) the occupants do not live and eat with any other persons in the building, and when there is either . . .

(2) a direct entrance from the outside or through a common hall . . . OR (3) a kitchen or cooking equipment only for the use of the occupants of that DU.

You must remember this definition of a DU so that you don't miss any DU's, and so that you don't list any group quarters.

b. Types of dwelling units you are likely to find (but remember that this list is merely a guide, and may have missed some places that should be considered as dwelling units):

--A single house which is intended for use by only one family.

--An apartment in a building which includes other apartments.

--A basement or attic apartment.

--Vacant houses or apartments which could be occupied.

--Hotel or motel rooms which are (1) occupied by "permanent" guests, or (2) occupied by employees who have no "permanent" residence elsewhere. In listing, indicate "permanent guest" or "employee" to help all interviewers who will work in the segment.

--Residential buildings under construction. In listing, tell us that such a building is under construction.

--Rooms within group quarters or an institution (such as a fraternity, halfway house, or dormitory) which are used as the permanent home of a staff member and is considered a dwelling unit according to our definition.

--A room in a non-residential building where there are no other rooms intended for residential use. Thus, if there is one room in a warehouse which the caretaker uses for his living quarters, such a room is considered a dwelling unit.

--A trailer, which is used as a permanent residence, and not just a vacation home.

--A trailer location in a trailer lot or park in which numbered spaces are rented. In such a trailer park, list each separate space to be used by one trailer as a DU even if no trailer occupies the space at the moment--that is, an empty trailer space in a regular trailer park should be treated like a vacant apartment or house.

--Work camps occupied by seasonal workers. Even if a worker occupies a unit for less than six months of the year, that unit should be listed, for it may become a permanent residence in the future.

--Seasonal dwellings. List summer homes, resort cottages, or other part-time homes which could serve as permanent residences, even if you know or suspect that the present occupant's main residence is elsewhere.

--Rooms occupied by boarders are separate DU's if they meet our definition of a DU. You will list the quarters occupied by each boarder on a separate line of the Dwelling Unit Listing Sheet. Thus if you run across a rooming house in which all the residents live and eat separately from each other and their rooms opened off a common hallway, you have found several dwelling units, each of which should be listed on a separate line of the DU listing sheet.

You have found only one dwelling unit, however, if you run into a boarding house at which the residents actually live and eat together. It is a Dwelling Unit only if there are four or fewer boarders living there. If there are five or more such residents, you may have run into group quarters, not a dwelling unit. Group quarters are described in the next sub-section.

c. For group quarters, which you do not list on the DULS, we follow again the Census Bureau definition. Five or more persons unrelated to the person in charge automatically makes what might have seemed to be one Dwelling Unit into Group Quarters. The following are group quarters, and are not to be listed:

--Boarding houses of 5 or more whose rooms cannot be considered as separate dwelling units.

--School or other institutional dormitories (but watch for the dwelling unit of a "house head" or permanent "dormitory counselor" or some such person).

--Fraternity houses.

--Barracks.

--Staff rooms in hospitals.

--Convents and monasteries.

d. "Non-residential" units, which are not to be listed: (However, you cannot completely ignore such institutions, since some of them may contain the dwelling unit of a manager, janitor, owner, etc.

--Hospitals.

--Transient hotels or motels.

--Prisons.

--Homes for the aged.

--Other institutions which provide care for residents or inmates.

--Unoccupied buildings which have been condemned or which are being torn down.

--Places of business such as stores, factories, etc.--but be sure to look for hard-to-find living quarters behind or above or inside business places.

--Resort cabins which can never be used for more than a short period each year.

RULE II List by inspection (chiefly).

Single-family houses can usually be spotted just by looking at the outside of the house. Sometimes, however, what appears to be a one-family house has been converted into a two- or three-family house. Since it is not always possible to tell this by looking at the outside of the house, you should inspect, briefly, the outside of each one-family house for multiple dwelling unit "signs." Some of the "signs" are: more than one mailbox; more than one electric or gas meter; more than one clothesline; several bells; or only one bell with instructions for signalling different apartments, as, for example: "Ring once for Smith," "Ring twice for Jones," etc; and no doubt you will find other "signs" when you are there.

You may also find it necessary at times to ask people whom you happen to see on the block whether any of the houses have more than one dwelling unit in them.

Most two-family houses are easy to spot, especially the ordinary side-by-side type or the kind with two floors with identical apartments on each.

In apartment houses you will usually be able to list all dwelling units from mailboxes or bells, or by walking around each floor. However, sometimes it will be necessary to get the information from the superintendent, janitor, or a tenant.

RULE III List in order.

We have provided a system which all listers should follow. This is to insure thoroughness in the listing and to help in finding the dwelling units when we return to these segments later on. Following this system will mean that the interviewer will be able to find the exact dwelling unit that you have entered on the listing sheet.

Start listing at the spot marked X on your map. Walk around the block in the direction of the arrow. List IN ORDER every dwelling unit until you return to the spot from which you started.

If you are following the arrows correctly you will discover that THE BUILDINGS WILL ALWAYS BE ON YOUR RIGHT as you walk around the block, and you will be walking in a clockwise direction.

Listing single and two-family houses has already been discussed. The following information is especially useful for listing in larger cities, where there is mostly multiple dwelling unit housing.

City Housing Projects: Most large projects have mailboxes with apartment numbers on them which are easy to read and are set up in a logical order (such as 1A, 1B, 1C, ID, 2A, etc.). Do the listing from the alphabet first (for example, Apartment A, Apt. B, C, etc.; or 1, 2, 3, 4, etc.; or 1A, 1B, 1C, 2A, 2B, 2C, etc.). IF YOU SHOULD FIND CITY HOUSING WHICH DOES NOT FIT THIS DESCRIPTION, CHECK WITH YOUR SUPERVISOR.

Tenements, brownstones and other apartment buildings:

A. IF APARTMENTS ARE CLEARLY IDENTIFIED ON MAILBOXES OR BELLS

Look at the mailboxes and bells. If you see that they are identified clearly in consecutive order by apartment number (that is, 1A, 1B, 2A, 2B, etc., or 1, 2, 3, 4, 5, etc.), record in the following way:

24	425 Howard Ave.	Apt. 1A			
25		1B			
26		1C			
27		1D - Smith			
28		2A			
29		2B - Jones			
30		2C - Clark			
31		2D - Johnson			
32		3A			
33		3B - E. Wilson			
34		3C			

B. IF APARTMENT NUMBERS ARE NOT CLEARLY IDENTIFIED ON MAILBOXES OR BELLS

If the apartment numbers are NOT clearly identified on the bells or mailboexes in any clear consecutive order, list by walking through the building, floor by floor.

Begin in the basement, and work each floor FROM THE BOTTOM OF THE BUILDING TO THE TOP OF THE BUILDING. For example, basement, to list floor, to 2nd floor, etc.

If there is more than one dwelling unit on each floor, start listing with THE DU ON YOUR RIGHT. This means your right side as you come off the elevator or as you come to the top step of the stairway leading to that floor or from the outside entrance of the building.

Proceed around the floor as you do around the block, keeping the apartments on your right as you list. As an example, refer the diagram on the next page, and see the proper way of recording that floor.

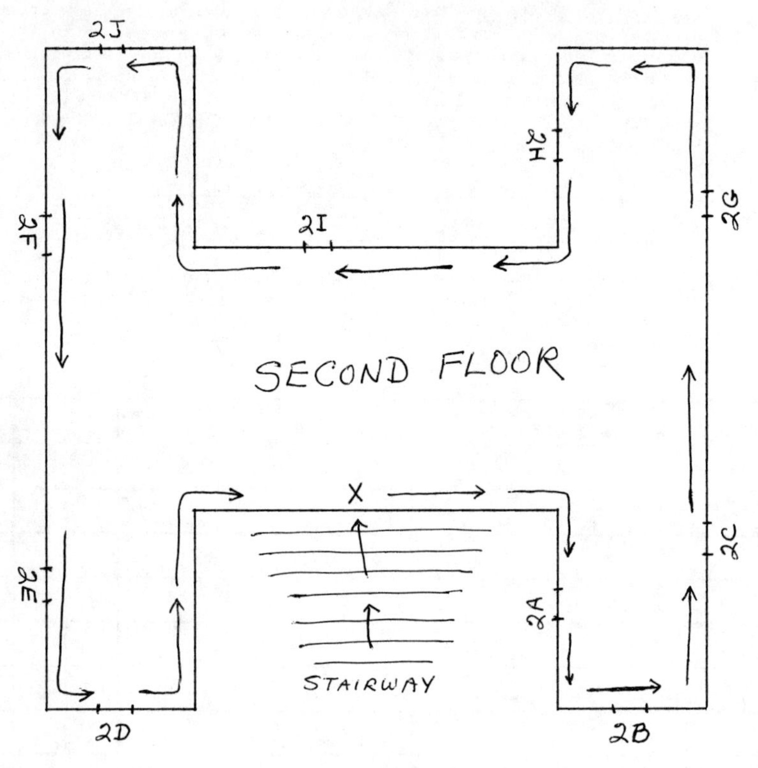

770 EMPIRE BLVD.

12	770 Empire Blvd.	2nd floor - Apt. 2A	N		
13		" " " 2B	"		
14		" " " 2C	"		
15		" " " 2G	"		
16		" " " 2H	"		
17		" " " 2I	"		
18		" " " 2J	"		
19		" " " 2F	"		
20		" " " 2E	"		
21		" " " 2D	"		

C. IF THE APARTMENTS ARE NOT CLEARLY IDENTIFIED ON MAILBOXES, BELLS, OR DOORS TO THE APARTMENTS

There may be some cases where there is no way of identifying the apartment even when you work from floor to floor, that is, there are no numbers on the doors or any other indication of what the apartment number or letter is.

In this case, you must describe the location of the apartment and anything you can about the door. For example, "Second floor, apt. immediately to the right of the stairway, with bell painted red on right side of door--Name, Garcia." The next apartment you may describe like this: "Second floor, on right of stairway, apt. to the left of Garcia's, with door painted blue and orange stripes--Name, Jones."

The most important thing is to give a description which makes it absolutely clear which dwelling unit on which floor you are talking about.

D. IF THE APARTMENTS ARE NOT CLEARLY IDENTIFIED ON MAILBOXES OR BELLS AND YOU CANNOT GET INTO THE BUILDING

If the apartment descriptions on the bells and mailboxes are unclear and you CAN'T GET INTO THE BUILDING to do the listing from each floor, then you must use whatever information is on the bells or mailboxes.

For example, suppose there are two rows of bells which look like this:

0 0 0 0 0 0 0 _______ top row

0 0 0 0 0 0 0 _______ bottom row

You should begin listing the bells using the rules we set up before: start with bottom row, right to left, then top row, right to left, indicating the position of the bell within the row. If there are any names next to the bells, enter them on the listing sheet.

The listing would look like this:

1	723 Saratoga Ave.	Bottom row of bells -- 1st bell from right			
2		Bottom row - 2nd bell from right			
3		" " 3rd " " "			
4		" " 4th " " "			
5		" " 5th " " "			
6		" " 6th " " "			
7		" " 7th " " "			
8		Top row - 1st " " "			
9		" " 2nd " " "			
10		" " 3rd " " "			
11		" " 4th " " "			

Another example. If the bells looked like this:

0	0	0 ←	5th row from bottom
0	0	0 ←	4th row from bottom
0	0	0 ←	3rd row from bottom
0	0	0 ←	2nd row from bottom
0	0	0 ←	Bottom

Enter identification of the row, then identification of position of bell within the row.

The listing would look like this:

1	1219 St. Johns Place	Bottom row of bells -- 1st bell from right			
2		2nd bell " " (middle)			
3		3rd " " "			
4		2nd row from bottom 1st bell from right			

. . . and so on.

RULE IV   Cover the entire area.

Every road, street, alley, court, or passageway in your segment should be covered, because there may be dwelling units hidden in them that you might otherwise miss. Since it is more likely to overlook such units, extra care is all the more important. Enter every alley, street, or road within your segment as you come to it, going down one side and back up the other side.

When you are listing in a housing development, note that the entrance of the building does not always face the street. You must therefore take extra care that all buildings are covered. Check house or building numbers to make sure that you haven't missed a building.

Dwelling units may be situated in such other unusual places as: in or behind stores, behind other units that face the street, over garages or stores, in factory yards, etc. It is important to include the dwelling units found in all such places.

RULE V   Keep strictly within the boundaries of the segment.

Where the boundary line follows a street or road, it is intended to run down the middle of that street or road so that you list all dwelling units on the side which falls inside your segment, but not those on the other side of the street or road segment.

RULE VI   Use one line for listing each dwelling unit.

Do not place two units on a single line. Never skip a line. Use the back of each sheet.

RULE VII   Identify each unit completely by its location.

List the address of each dwelling unit in full detail. List each individual dwelling unit on the "Dwelling Unit Listing Sheet" in the column headed "Name and Address or Description of Dwelling Unit." Describe the unit in such a complete way that you or anyone else could find it in the future. Make sure that someone else would know exactly which rooms are included in the unit and which are not included. If there is a house number, use it, plus any additional description which may be necessary. Where there are no numbers, describe the house as clearly as possible, e.g., "Spruce Street, large house, second from corner, red brick," "Spruce Street, near alley, small white house with uncovered porch," etc. If an unnumbered house is located next door to a numbered house, or between two numbered houses, describe it this way: "Large red brick house between 1918 Spring Ave. and 1934 Spring Ave., immediately next door to 1918 Spring."

Complete street names should always be used. Do not leave out the words "street," "place," "boulevard," etc. When the same address applies to several dwelling units, ditto marks should be used rather than writing the numbers or words over again. However, add to each unit enough identification to distinguish it clearly from all other units with the same or similar address. Do not leave the space blank in such a case since this might be taken for something left out.

Always give apartment or room number in apartment houses. Where apartments are numbered or lettered, write in floor and exact location of room or apartment (right, left, back, etc.). If more than one sleeping room on a floor is rented out to lodgers, describe each separate unit carefully, by giving its location--for example, "1519 Sherman Ave. --second floor, sleeping room on right side of building, directly behind stairway."

If a dwelling unit is in an alley with no name, describe the alley in some way so that there can be no mistake in finding it in the future (for example, "off 15th Street, between Buchanan and Johnson, running North-East").

For a sample of the proper way to list various types of dwelling units, see Appendix I in the back of these instructions.

RULE VIII   Indicate race of occupants in column "Negro or white."

Enter "N" for Negro and "W" for white or any race other than Negro. Do not ring doorbells to determine the race of the occupants. Record your best guess, based on your knowledge of the area or neighborhood. You may use ditto marks if the segment seems to be mainly one race.

RULE IX **Language.**

If, by observing the neighborhood, you have reason to believe that a foreign language may be spoken there, be alert for which language it is, and record--again, by observation only--in the proper column.

RULE X **Names of occupants.**

If Dwelling Units are not numbered or lettered, and if in addition to a description such as "2nd floor right front" you are able to provide the name of the occupant, then do so. But do not ring doorbells to obtain names. These should only be entered if they can readily be copied off nameplates or mailboxes.

RULE XI **Write clearly.**

The listing forms are a permanent record from which samples of dwelling units will be chosen. If the entries are not written clearly and accurately, we will not be able to identify the dwelling units drawn from the lists; for instance, when writing is unclear, it is easy to confuse the figure "2" with "3," or "6" with "0,' or "3" with "5," and it will be difficult for an interviewer to find the address.

C. Enter Total Number of DU's

As you list a segment, number consecutively all the lines on which dwelling units are listed. The first DULS used has printed line numbers. You will have to number the lines you use on any continuation sheets you use. The last line number should be equal to the total number of dwelling units in the segment. Enter this number in the space provided for "Total DU's" in the box near the upper right-hand corner of the first page of the Dwelling Unit Listing Sheet.

D. Draw Each Non-Residential Building on the Sketch Map for the Segment

Each non-residential building (for example, schools, churches, factories, etc.) should be drawn in on your sketch map so that you or another interviewer can use this data to help you find dwelling units in the future. Simply sketch in the approximate shape and size of such buildings and label them clearly--for example, "high school."

EVEN THOUGH THESE INSTRUCTIONS ARE VERY DETAILED, YOU MAY RUN INTO SOME PROBLEMS WHICH HAVE NOT BEEN EXPLAINED. THESE SPECIAL PROBLEMS SHOULD BE BROUGHT TO THE ATTENTION OF THE SUPERVISOR TO BE SURE YOU HANDLE THEM CORRECTLY.

APPENDIX

Page 1 of 4 Pages

DWELLING UNIT LISTING SHEET (DULS)

NORC
F-78A
4/68

Segment No. 456

City Study Town Census Tract 565 Block(s) 4

DIAGRAM OF SEGMENT

(Start at the "X" and follow the arrows which show the direction for listing.)

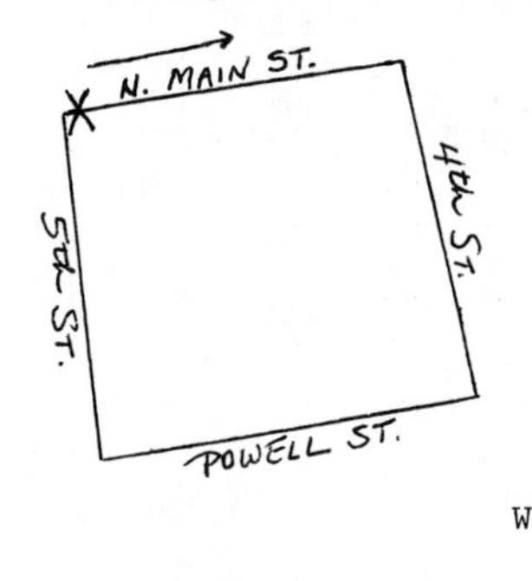

N
W E
S

(Fill this in after completing the listing.)
Lister's Name Elliott Doe

Date 5/9/68 Total DU's 40

List every DU located within this segment. Start at the "X" and go in order around the segment. Go in and out of each street, alley, or road within the segment as you come to it. Continue until you have reached your starting point again. Use one line for each DU.

BE SURE THAN EVERY PLACE OF RESIDENCE IS LISTED AND THAT ALL APARTMENTS, ETC., ARE NUMBERED OR OTHERWISE IDENTIFIED SO THAT SOMEONE ELSE COULD FIND THIS PARTICULAR DU.

Line No.	NAME AND ADDRESS OR DESCRIPTION OF DWELLING UNIT Indicate house number and street name. Identify apartments by floor, number, and location. If this is not possible, describe dwelling unit and its location in detail. Also enter the name of the resident of those DU's for which there are no apartment numbers.		Negro or White	Language	Assignment Line
	Street Address	Apt. No. or Name, if necessary			
1	1 N. Main St.	Bsmt. apt.			
2	" " " "	Grd. floor			
3	" " " "	2nd floor			
4	" " " "	3rd floor			
5	3 N. Main St.	(1)			
6	7 N. Main St.	Bsmt. - front			
7	" " " "	" - rear			
8	" " " "	Grd. floor - right (2)			
9	" " " "	" " - left			

(OVER)

Page 2 of 4 Pages

LISTING CONTINUATION SHEET

NORC
F-78A
4/68

Segment No. 456

Line No.	NAME AND ADDRESS OR DESCRIPTION OF DWELLING UNIT Indicate house number and street name. Identify apartments by floor, number, and location. If this is not possible, describe dwelling unit and its location in detail. Also enter the name of the resident of those DU's for which there are no apartment numbers.		Negro or White	Language	Assignment Line
	Street Address	Apt. No. or Name, if necessary			
10	7 N. Main St.	2nd floor - right			
11	" " " "	" " - left			
12	9 N. Main St.	Grd. floor Apt. #1			
13	" " " "	" " " #2			
14	" " " "	2nd floor #101			
15	" " " "	" " #102			
16	11 N. Main St.	Apt. A			
17	" " " "	" B			
18	1st DU just north of 11 N. Main (3) frame house with stone porch rail & chimney				
19	19 N. Main St.	South side (or right side)			
20	" " " "	Center entrance			
21	" " " "	North side (or left side)			
22	21 N. Main St.	Grd. floor-room-right-front			
23	" " " "	" " " " rear			
24	" " " "	" " apt. left rear			
25	" " " "	2nd floor-room-front-right			

(Use a continuation sheet, if necessary)

Page 3 of 4 Pages

LISTING CONTINUATION SHEET

NORC
F-78A
4/68

Segment No. 456

City Study Town Census Tract 565 Block(s) 4

Line No.	NAME AND ADDRESS OR DESCRIPTION OF DWELLING UNIT Indicate house number and street name. Identify apartments by floor, number, and location. If this is not possible, describe dwelling unit and its location in detail. Also enter the name of the resident of those DU's for which there are no apartment numbers.		Negro or White	Language	Assignment Line
	Street Address	Apt. No. or Name, if necessary			
26	21 N. Main St.	2nd floor-room-front-left			
27	" " " "	" " " rear-right			
28	" " " "	" " " " left			
29	" " " "	3rd floor apt.			
30	23 N. Main St.	Grd. + 2nd floors (4) entrance from outside			
31	" " " "	(4) 2nd floor-room-near stairs			
32	27 N. Main St.	Grd. floor			
33	" " " "	2nd floor-room-front			
34	" " " "	2nd fl. room-1st door from front DU			
35	" " " "	" " " 2nd door from front DU			
36	" " " "	" " " rear			
37	29 N. Main St.	left side of door (5) left doorbell			
38	" " " "	left side of door right doorbell			
39	" " " "	right side of door left doorbell			
40	" " " "	right side of door right doorbell			

(Use another continuation sheet, if necessary)

LISTING CONTINUATION SHEET

NORC
F-78A
4/68

Segment No. 456

Line No.	NAME AND ADDRESS OR DESCRIPTION OF DWELLING UNIT Indicate house number and street name. Identify apartments by floor, number, and location. If this is not possible, describe dwelling unit and its location in detail. Also enter the name of the resident of those DU's for which there are no apartment numbers.		Negro or White	Language	Assignment Line
	Street Address	Apt. No. or Name, if necessary			
(1)	Single family DU, requires no more information than this.				
(2)	Distinction here might be front and rear, rather than left and right.				
(3)	Where it is absolutely impossible to get a street number, get full description of DU and indicate specific location with reference to the nearest numbered DU.				
(4)	Example of listing of DU occupied by single family plus roomer (not related to family). The room has a separate entrance and its occupant does not eat with the family occupying the rest of the house.				
(5)	Where obvious from number of doorbells that there are several DU's in building but you cannot ascertain their exact location, distinguish DU's by position of doorbells or by numbers assigned to doorbells.				

(Use another continuation sheet, if necessary)

NORC
4052
5-69

EXTRA DWELLING UNIT REPORT

City: ______________________ Date: ______________________

Interviewer's Name: ______________________

Today I found extra dwelling units at:

Segment #: _______ Line #: _______

Address, as shown on DULS: ______________________

Number of extra DU's found at this line: ____________

GIVE A CORRECT ADDRESS OR DESCRIPTION FOR EACH DU FOUND AT THIS LINE:

NEW LINE NUMBERS AND DESCRIPTIONS:

_____ A. ______________________

_____ B. ______________________

_____ C. ______________________

_____ D. ______________________

_____ E. ______________________

If more than 5 units are at this address continue recording them, but do not interview at any line until you receive instructions from the office.

_____ F. ______________________

_____ G. ______________________

_____ H. ______________________

_____ I. ______________________

_____ J. ______________________

APPENDIX D

SURVEY MATERIALS

LETTER TO RESPONDENTS

COMPREHENSIVE HEALTH CENTER
1070 WASHINGTON STREET, S. W.
ATLANTA, GEORGIA 30315

June, 1968

Dear Community Resident:

The Comprehensive Health Center is talking with one thousand families in the area about health problems and other information which will help them better plan their services to meet the needs of the entire community.

An interviewer will bring this letter to you, and we would greatly appreciate your cooperation. Your opinions are important, and all information you give will be kept in strict confidence. The interviewer carries an identification card signed by us.

We wish to thank you in advance for your time and interest in this important project.

Sincerely yours,

Calvin A. Brown, Jr., M.D.
Co-Director

William M. Marine, M.D.
Co-Director

CAB/WMM:am

NORC
4055
9/68

RED HOOK HEALTH SURVEY

HOUSEHOLD FOLDER

DWELLING UNIT DESCRIPTION

ADDRESS: ____________________ SEGMENT # ________

DULS LINE # ________

CITY: ____________________

TOTAL # PERSONS IN HOUSEHOLD

APT. # OR DESCRIPTION: ____________________

RECORD OF ALL CALLS ON HOUSEHOLD					
Date	Day	Time	Phone or Personal	Results of Call	Interviewer

(INSIDE OF

FOLDER)

USE THIS PAGE TO KEEP TRACK OF SEPARATE BOOKLETS, IF YOU DO NOT TURN IN ALL BOOKLETS REQUIRED FOR A HOUSEHOLD AT THE SAME TIME.

A. # of Blue/Pink booklets required in household: __________

B.

# of B/P booklets turned in to office	... On (date)

C. Total # B/P booklets completed in this household: __________

NOTE: If total # booklets completed is less than # required, be sure to make out a Non-Interview Report explaining reason.

D. Main Questionnaire turned in on: ____________________
(date)

SURVEY SRS-4055
9-68

NATIONAL OPINION RESEARCH CENTER
University of Chicago

RED HOOK NEIGHBORHOOD HEALTH CENTER SURVEY

SPECIFICATIONS PART I

General and Administrative Instructions

TABLE OF CONTENTS

A. YOUR EMPLOYER, RED HOOK NEIGHBORHOOD HEALTH CENTER

The purposes of the Center are:

1. To bring a much needed program of health services right to the community.
2. To hire and train people of the community to work at the Center.

B. PURPOSE OF THE SURVEY

This is a study to help the new neighborhood health center learn about the people who live in the area. We need to collect information about people's health problems and the kinds of medical care they have been getting. This is necessary for planning the kinds of medical services that are needed in the community and to see how well the community is now providing these services.

After a few years another study can be made and by comparing people's health problems and the places they go to for medical care at that time with the information we get now, the center and the community can see how effective the center really is. For example -- Are the older people in the community using the health center as much as they should?

C. ABOUT NORC

The National Opinion Research Center is non-profit organization connected with the University of Chicago. It conducts many kinds of surveys of interest to social scientists, foundations, and government agencies.

NORC has been asked to act as consultants in conducting this study in Red Hook. It will be working as well on neighborhood health center studies in other parts of the United States. There will then be available the experiences for all these communities that each one can learn from.

D. THE SAMPLE OF HOUSEHOLDS TO BE INTERVIEWED

The sample consists of 1800 dwelling units selected in the area served by the Red Hook Neighborhood Health Center. A "dwelling unit" is the same as a "household." The dwelling units were chosen on a scientific basis in such a way that they represent the entire population covered by the new Health Center.

It is, therefore, very important that we get an interview in each assigned dwelling unit.

E. YOUR RESPONDENT (THE PERSON WHO ANSWERS YOUR QUESTIONS)

This should be the person who knows the most about the health of all members of the household. It is usually the mother. Others in the household who happen to be home at the time of the interview, such as husband or children, can be asked to take part in answering factual questions, especially those that have to do with their own health. If your respondent does not know about a member of the household, you will ask this person about himself. Also, if there is any adult person in the household who is not related to the respondent (a boarder, for instance) you will always ask this person about himself. If he is not home at the time of the main interview, find out when he is at home and plan to return to the house at that time.

F. DWELLING UNIT LISTING SHEETS (DULS)

The Dwelling Unit Listing Sheet is a list of all the dwelling units (households) in a square block (called a segment).

You will receive a copy of the Dwelling Unit Listing Sheets for each segment in your assignment. These sheets will help you to find the exact location of your assigned households. An "X" in the right-hand column of your listing sheet means that the household listed on that line will be interviewed.

G. YOUR ASSIGNED HOUSEHOLDS AND THE HOUSEHOLD FOLDER

You will have a separate Household Folder for each household in your assignment. Use this folder to hold all of the materials for that interview. At the upper right-hand corner you will find the Segment Number in which the dwelling unit is located, the Dwelling Unit Line Number from which the address was taken, and a four-digit number entered in the boxes at the top. All of these numbers together become the Case Number and all of them must be recorded on the Main Questionnaire and the supplements.

Each household interview will consist of:

1. A Main Questionnaire to get general background information on the household and detailed health information on your respondent.

2. A shorter questionnaire called a "supplement" for health information on each other member of the household.

If you are unable to complete your interview at one time (because your respondent does not have all the information about some members of the household or you still have to do an interview with an unrelated adult):

1. Bring the Main Questionnaire and all of the completed supplements to the office.

2. Keep the Household Folder with the blank supplements to complete the case. Be sure that the necessary identification information (segment, dwelling unit listing numbers, case number, person's name and number) are on each supplement you still must do.

3. Record on the back of the Household Folder the supplements you still must complete in that household.

4. When you complete all the supplements, turn them in together with the Household Folder for that household.

H. DWELLING UNIT DESCRIPTION

The dwelling unit description on the Household Folder is made up of the address and the apartment number or description of your assigned dwelling unit (also called household).

Unfortunately we have not always been able to obtain an apartment number. To help you locate dwelling units without apartment numbers, we would like you to know what the lister was told to do when the apartment numbers were not available. If she was able to enter the building and list by walking on each floor, she was told to list in the following order:

1. Bottom to top (that is, basement to ground floor to second).
2. Right to left within each floor.
3. Front to the back on any given side of the floor.

This instruction bottom to top, right to left, front to back, permitted her to handle all dwelling units in the same way.

She called the street floor the "ground floor," and always used "second floor" for dwellings one flight up.

The terms "right" and "left" should always refer to your right and left as you stand in front of the main entrance to the building and face the building.

If your dwelling unit description says 4th mailbox (or bell) from right, it will require careful searching on your part to be certain that you interview in the correct dwelling unit.

When you find the bell or mailbox which is described on your Household Folder, look for the dwelling unit which it belongs to. Sometimes it is impossible to tell which apartment belongs to the bell or mailbox. In such a case, ask the superintendent or another resident which door it is. IF THERE IS STILL ANY DOUBT IN YOUR MIND that you have found the right household, discuss it with your supervisor before conducting the interview.

I. A DWELLING UNIT

We have been using the term "Dwelling Unit" and this is a good place to explain exactly what a Dwelling Unit is.

A Dwelling Unit (DU) is a single room or group of rooms that is meant for separate living quarters. That means that the people who live in this single room or group of rooms do not live and eat with any other persons in the building AND

1. There is a separate door that leads only to this room or group of rooms.

OR

2. There is a separate kitchen or cooking equipment for the use of these people only.

This is important to know because:

1) You may find, for example, on your Household Folder that the Dwelling Unit you have to visit has been listed only as "Second Floor." You get there and you see that on the second floor, there are two doors, or two bells, or two separate names. You would immediately suspect that you really have two separate Dwelling Units. If you find out, after asking around, that there are two separate Dwelling Units, you have found an extra Dwelling Unit and you will have to complete two separate interviews, one in each of these separate Dwelling Units.

2) Or else when you see "Second Floor," you may find two doors but you are not so sure that they are two separate Dwelling Units. You would then have to find out whether one of those doors leads to a room that is occupied by a roomer who might be considered to have his own Dwelling Unit according to the definition we gave above.

By that definition, there is a separate door that leads directly to his rooms, he does not have to go through any of their rooms in order to enter his room, and he does not live and eat with the other household members. This again would be considered a separate Dwelling Unit and you will be required to conduct a separate interview with the person living in this separate Dwelling Unit.

If a roomer has to go through at least some of the apartment of other people in order to get to this room OR takes his meals with the people in this apartment, the person would be listed with all the other people who live in this group of rooms and would be included in their interview.

3) If you find up to 4 extra DUs: We have given you blank Household Folders. Enter the same identifying numbers -- segment number, DU line number and 4-digit number in boxes, and add a letter "A" for the first one, "B" for the second, "C" for the third, "D" for the fourth extra Dwelling Unit after the DU line number.

In addition, an "extra dwelling unit report form" must be made out for each of these additional DUs.

4) If you find more than 4 extra DUs, do not do any interviews in any of these households. Make out an "extra DU report form," write down the information, and return this form to your supervisor.

Please remember that if you have any problems, your supervisor will help you.

J. ADMINISTRATIVE MATTERS

1. Keeping in Touch with the Office

Your supervisors are Margot Karp and Dolores Sanjurjo. You will be expected to come to the Information Center at 783 Hicks Street daily until your supervisor tells you something else.

Bring with you all completed work and a Time and Expense Sheet for each day that you worked on the study. This daily visit to the office will give you an opportunity to discuss any problems or questions that may have come up during the day before. If you are unable to come in for any reason when you are expected, you must call the office. The telephone numbers are: 780-1401 and 780-1402.

2. Forms and Supplies Used in this Study

The Transmittal Sheet: This sheet lists how much of each kind of supply you should find in your envelopes. Your first job is to see if you received all the things you were supposed to. If you are short of any supplies, tell your supervisor when you come to the office the next day.

Blank Questionnaires: Main Questionnaires (white)
Blue supplements to be used for people 14 and over.
Pink supplements to be used for children under 14.

Cards for certain questions: There are two cards, A and B, which you will need in the course of an interview.

Household Folders: with addresses for each household in your assignment.

Extra blank Household Folders to be used when you find extra households in what we thought was only one household.

Extra Dwelling Unit Report Forms: to be filled out every time you find an additional Dwelling Unit where only one was thought to be.

Dwelling Unit Listing Sheets (DULS)

Non-interview Report Forms: A Non-interview Report Form will be filled out by you and returned to the office whenever you cannot complete an interview or a supplement in your assignment.

Time and Expense Sheets: Directions on how to fill them out will be found in the Employees Manual. You have all been given copies of this manual.

Pre-interview Questionnaire: This is to be filled out by every interviewer before doing the first interview. Here is a chance for you to be a respondent!

Post-interview Questionnaire: This is to be filled out by every interviewer after all the interviewing is finished.

Identification Cards: You will be carrying with you an ID card from the Red Hood Neighborhood Health Center. Be careful not to leave it anywhere.

Letters from the Red Hook Neighborhood Health Center: They will explain why you are there and should be given to your respondent. They can also be left at the household with a note as to when you will call again if the respondent is not at home when you go there the first time.

Printed matter describing the Red Hook Neighborhood Health Center and its services: To be left at each household.

Mimeographed sheet telling about other social services and health care: To be left with the respondents who have asked for help or advice.

K. GENERAL RULES ABOUT HOW TO PROCEED

1. Preparing for the Field

Whenever you go into the field, take all of your Household Folders with you because if one or two respondents are not at home or are not ready to be interviewed at that time, you can then make calls at the other homes in your assignment. Even if you have an appointment with a respondent for the interview and can only do one interview that day, take along more Household Folders and questionnaires in case the respondent has to break the appointment.

Make sure that you have enough sharpened pencils and the cards for the card questions before you leave home, as well as the letter describing the survey and your ID card.

2. No Substitutions Allowed

You must interview only the persons who live at your assigned household.

3. Do Not Interview Anyone You Know

If you happen to know any of the respondents assigned to you, no matter how slightly, do not interview them. Fill out the Non-interview Report Form and return the Household Folder to the office and we will send another interviewer.

Nearly all respondents will be willing to discuss all matters very freely with an unknown professional interviewer from a respectable research organization. But if the interviewer is also a friend of hers, or known to be on close terms with some other friends of hers, then the professional relationship no longer exists.

4. Language Problems

If you will be interviewing only in English, you may come across a respondent who speaks only Spanish, or some other language. In such instances, fill out the Non-interview Report Form and return the Household Folder to the office. We will send an interviewer who speaks the language or arrange for an interpreter. You must not use a neighbor or a relative to translate for the respondent unless you receive permission to do so from your supervisor.

5. Not at Home

If no one is home on your first call, you must call back at the household at a different time of day and on a different day of the week. For instance, if you called on a Monday morning and found no one at home, try again on a Tuesday or Wednesday afternoon.

Each time you make a call to a respondent you must write down the time and the result of the call in the RECORD OF CALLS section of the Household Folder. It is always useful to you to refer to the Record of Calls when you are working with many interviews, since your past visits to that household should tell you when are the best and worst times to call. Also, if another interviewer has to take over the interview, or you have to take over another interviewer's work, this Record of Calls should save you a lot of wasted steps and time.

Make at least three calls to the household at different times and days of the week. If you happen to be in the neighborhood for another case, be sure to stop by and see if anyone is at home. Ask the neighbors or the superintendent to tell you when someone in that household is usually at home.

If after three calls and detective work, and another visit while you are in the neighborhood, you still cannot find the respondent at home, fill out a Non-interview Report Form and return the Household Folder to the office.

6. The Introduction To Be Used

Use the introduction that appears on the questionnaire. The introduction is short and intended to be that way. Always introduce yourself as briefly as possible. In the vast majority of cases the short introduction is enough. Do not say any more unless asked. Get into the questions as quickly as possible in order to save time and avoid possible objection to being interviewed.

7. How To Answer Questions and Objections

In most cases your brief introduction will tell the respondent all she needs or wants to know about the survey, and you can go right on with the interview.

In some cases, however, the respondent may want additional information or may raise some objections to being interviewed. Refer your respondent to the letter from the Red Hook Neighborhood Health Center or you may, of course, read the letter for her.

If the respondent says, "How do I know you're not selling something," tell her that we have absolutely nothing to sell -- "all we are interested in is talking to you about health matters."

If she asks what the survey is about or what kind of survey it is, say "It's a survey to get information to plan for health services in this neighborhood. The first question is . . . ."

8. How To Handle Refusals

You should find very few persons refusing to be interviewed.

If you do run across refusals, explain to the person how important her participation is. Tell her that in order to make the best plans and programs at the Red Hook Neighborhood Health Center, it is important to get an accurate and true picture of all the households which fall into the sample.

If we lose the information from those who are too busy or those who cannot be bothered we will not have a true picture of every kind of person.

If she refuses to be interviewed, despite your attempts to persuade her, fill out a Non-interview Report Form telling us what happened. We will probably try sending a letter and then ask you or another interviewer to try again.

If the person does not refuse you outright but keeps putting you off by telling you to come back again and again, or doesn't keep her appointments with you, fill out a Non-interviewer Report Form after you have made three attempts to interview her.

Accept refusals and broken appointments gracefully. You must maintain a pleasant relationship with every respondent at all times, no matter how "difficult" you think she is. Be polite and businesslike at all times. Under no circumstances should you lose your temper, no matter how justified you think you are.

For all those who refuse or cannot be reached, always try to give us the fullest information on the Non-interview Report Form. If there is not enough room, attach another page to it. We will use all of this information in trying to get the person to cooperate.

L. INTERVIEWING TECHNIQUES

1. Your Relationship to the Respondent

You must be neutral at all times you are in contact with the respondent. The minute you begin to become personally involved with the respondent you will lose control of the interviewing situation.

You must show no shock or surprise at things you may hear.

2. Ask the Questions in a Natural Way

Our questions bring up such things as recent pregnancies, marital status, etc. You must remember that they have been designed by professional people and are there for a worthwhile purpose. We have had no problems with these questions in the past when the interviewer approaches them with the same matter-of-fact, professional tone that she uses with any other questions.

3. Other People Present during the Interview

It may prove helpful to have other household members around while you are interviewing. They may remember some important facts that the respondent has forgotten or does not know. It is all right to obtain your answers to factual questions in this way.

4. Ask All Questions Exactly as They Are Worded

Experience has shown that even changing one word can change the meaning of the question in the mind of the respondent.

5. Ask All Questions in the Same Order as They Appear

Ask all the questions in the order in which they appear in the questionnaire. We must be certain that all our respondents hear the questions in the same order.

6. Assure the Respondent that Her Answers Are Confidential

Take advantage of any opportunity to assure the respondent that the interview is confidential, and that she may speak freely without fear. Explain that we interview people all the time on many questions, and it's part of your job never to talk about any of the answers you receive. Assure her that her answers, along with those of hundreds of other individuals, will be keypunched and become statistics, and nobody else will ever see them, except people related to the survey.

Sometimes an otherwise cooperative respondent will refuse to answer a particular question, mumbling a "don't know" or saying, "I don't have to answer that." This gives you a good opportunity to say again: "Well, I want you to know that anything you tell me is seen by nobody except the people in our office." Then add, "We really need answers to that question from everyone we interview" and if it's an attitude question, "Can you just tell me generally how you feel about that?" Or if it's a factual question, "Can you give me just a rough idea?"

Obviously, if the respondent again refuses, do not press her, but go right to the next question.

And be sure to treat all answers as confidential. Some of the things the respondents tell you may surprise or interest you very much. It may be a temptation to pass them on to your spouse or friends.

It is your professional responsibility to resist this temptation, and to keep entirely to yourself any of the responses you get.

7. Do Not Answer Questions or Give Advice about Medical Care, Housing, Etc.

During the interview, some respondents may come to regard you as an expert on health matters. They may figure you have a great deal of knowledge if you spend your time interviewing people about these things. Therefore, they may occasionally ask you such questions as, "Do you think I should see a doctor about my cough?" or "Do you think _____ Hospital is a good place to go?" etc. Remember you may do more harm than good by offering advice. In these cases just leave a copy of the mimeographed sheet telling about social services and health care. This sheet has the answers to most of the questions you will be asked. If there are any questions that are not answered, ask the respondent to call the health survey office.

8. Edit Each Interview Right After You Finish It

As soon as possible after you leave each household, fill out the information on the back pages of the questionnaire, and then read through the interview while it's still fresh in your mind.

Fix up any handwriting that isn't clear.

9. If you have any problems, speak to your supervisor.

CONFIDENTIAL

Approved through-June 30, 1969

4055
9-68

Form approved.
Budget Bureau No. 116-R0146

NATIONAL OPINION RESEARCH CENTER
University of Chicago

OFFICE OF ECONOMIC OPPORTUNITY

NEIGHBORHOOD HEALTH CENTER SURVEY

→ Question - by - Question Specifications ←

BEGIN DECK 06

This 4-digit number appears on the Household Folder. Be sure to enter it on all questionnaires you use for this household -- the main and any Pink or Blue Quex you use.

| | | | | 1-4

05-06/RR

These numbers are found on the D.U.L.S. and on the Household Folder. Be sure to enter them on all quex you use for the household.

SEGMENT # _______________ 07-09

DULS LINE # _______________ 10-13

INTRODUCTION

Hello, I'm (YOUR NAME). We are conducting a health survey in this community. I'd like to speak to the lady of the house--or whoever knows about the health experience of the people in this household.

DECK 06

Note the time →

TIME INTERVIEW BEGAN:	____________	AM PM

1. How long have you and the others in this household lived here, at this address?
RECORD LONGEST TIME ANY HOUSEHOLD MEMBER HAS LIVED HERE. PROBE FOR BEST GUESS. → For example:

If a father who lives here now was born in this house -- but the R. and her husband have lived here only one year -- you would circle code 6, for "Ten years or more."

If the R. has trouble thinking of the length of time, you may read the code categories as probes -- we don't need exact amounts; just a general time period.

Less than 6 months	1	14/y
6 months to less than one year . .	2	
One year to less than three	3	
Three years to less than five . . .	4	
Five years to less than ten	5	
Ten years or more (SKIP TO Q. 4) .	6	

---

2. How long have you and the others in this household lived in this neighborhood?
RECORD LONGEST TIME ANY HOUSEHOLD MEMBER HAS LIVED HERE. PROBE FOR BEST GUESS.

Same as Q. 1.

Less than one year	1	15/y
One year to less than three	2	
Three years to less than five . . .	3	
Five years to less than ten	4	
Ten years or more (SKIP TO Q. 4) .	5	

---

3. And how long have you and the others in this household lived in New York City?
RECORD LONGEST TIME ANY HOUSEHOLD MEMBER HAS LIVED IN NEW YORK. PROBE FOR BEST GUESS.

Same as Q. 1.

Less than one year	6	16/y
One year to less than three	7	
Three years to less than five . . .	8	
Five years to less than ten	9	
Ten years or more	0	

DECK 06

If there is any difficulty in determining who is the Head of the Household -- refer to the "Spex Supplement" for further instructions.

	17-18

4. Now I'm going to ask about the health of all the members of this household, so I have to find out who lives here. Let's start with you, and your family, and then anyone else who lives here.

PERSON NUMBER	A. What is your name? ENTER R'S NAME ON LINE 00. Who else lives here? ENTER NAME(S) ON FOLLOWING LINE(S). PROBE BEFORE ASKING B-E: Have we missed anyone--persons who usually live here, but who are away from home now--travelling, on vacation, in a hospital or somewhere else? Have we missed any babies or small children?	B. What was (PERSON'S) age on (his/her) last birthday? ENTER AGE	C. RECORD RELATIONSHIP TO RESPONDENT FOR EACH PERSON. (ASK, IF NECESSARY)	D. CODE SEX. M	F	E. RECORD "HEAD" ON HEAD OF HOUSEHOLD'S LINE. (IF NECESSARY ASK: Who is the head of the household?) ENTER A CHECK (✓) ON LINES OF ANY PERSONS WHO ARE NOT RELATED TO HEAD OR WIFE OF HEAD.
00	This covers persons who have been away for 19-20		21 RESPONDENT	1	2	22
01	less than 90 days, and still consider this 23-24		25	1	2	26
02	their permanent residence, and plan 27-28		29	1	2	30
03	to return. 31-32	"Relationship," here in "C," means not	33	1	2	34
04	35-36	only blood or legal relationships	37	1	2	38
05	39-40	--but also such things as "roomer,"	41	1	2	42 "Relationship" here in "E" refers
06	43-44	"friend," etc. NOTE: This asks	45	1	2	46 only to blood or legal relation-
07	47-48	for relationship to the Respondent.	49	1	2	50 ships - such as, "son," "aunt,"
08	51-52		53	1	2	54 "father-in-law," etc.
09	55-56		57	1	2	58 NOTE: This refers to
10	59-60		61	1	2	62 relationship to the Head or
11	63-64		65	1	2	66 Head's wife.

The number you enter in this box will tell you the number of pink and/or blue supplements you will have to fill out for this household. LAST LINE NUMBER USED IS: [ ]

BEGIN DECK 01
05-06/00

Now to health matters. I'll be asking these questions about each member of the household. We'll start with you.

5. In general, would you say your own health is excellent, good, fair, or poor?

Excellent . . .	1	07/y
Good	2	
Fair	3	
Poor	4	
Don't know . .	5	

See "Spex Supplement" for further information about this question.

6. Who do you see, or where do you go, most of the time when you want to see a doctor for yourself--to what doctor or place?

NAME OF DOCTOR OR PLACE: If R. mentions both a doctor and a place at the same time ("Dr. Smith at the Union Health Center")--record all of this on the "name" line. 08/

ADDRESS OR DESCRIPTION: If R. doesn't know exact address, probe for description, such as, "corner of 102nd and 6th avenue," or "on 2nd Ave, between 89th & 90th." If not in Brooklyn, record city.

Be sure to code location, as well as entering address above. → CODE LOCATION:

In community . . .	6	09/y
Out of community .	7	
Never goes anywhere . . (SKIP TO Q. 12) . . .	8	

7. IF OBVIOUS, CODE WITHOUT ASKING: Is that a private doctor, a hospital clinic or emergency room, a chiropractor, a union or H.I.P. doctor or what?

Private doctor . . . (ASK A)	1	10/
Hospital clinic or emergency room . .	2	
Chiropractor	3	
Union or H.I.P. doctor . (ASK A) . .	4	
Other (SPECIFY)	5	

A. IF PRIVATE, UNION, OR H.I.P. DOCTOR: Is he a general practitioner or some kind of specialist?

General practitioner . .	7	11/y
Specialist . (ASK [1]) .	8	
Don't know	9	

[1] IF SPECIALIST: What kind of specialist is he?

If R. does not know the name of the specialty, try to find out what part of the body, or what kinds of people, the doctor deals with. 12/

Examples: "skin doctor", "baby doctor"

DECK 01

If both a doctor and a place were recorded on the "name" line in Q. 6, read only the name of the place here.

8. When did you first start going to (DOCTOR OR PLACE NAMED IN Q. 6)--within the last 12 months or longer ago than that?

Within last 12 months . .	1	13/y
Longer ago than that . . .	2	

---

9. OMITTED 14/R

---

10. How long does it usually take you to get there (the way you usually go)?

Read this phrase if the R. says it depends on how she goes.

0-9 minutes	1	15/y
10-19 minutes	2	
20-29 minutes	3	
30-39 minutes	4	
40-49 minutes	5	
50-59 minutes	6	
1 hour or more	7	
Never went from this address . .	8	
Never went . . (SKIP TO Q. 12) .	9	

---

11. Once you get there, about how long do you usually have to wait to see the doctor?

Suggested probe: "On the average, how long would you say you have to wait?"

Less than 1/2 hour	1	16/y
1/2 to less than one hour . . .	2	
One to less than 1-1/2 hours. .	3	
More than 1-1/2 hours	4	

DECK 01

12. Of all the doctors and places you know of, when something worries you about your own health, is there any one doctor or place that you trust more than any other, to get medical help or advice? (DO NOT PROBE.)

See "Spex Supplement." Also see these spex, for Q. 6.

Yes . . (ASK A) . . . . . 1 — 17/y

No . (SKIP TO Q. 17) . . 2

A. IF YES: What doctor or place?

NAME OF DOCTOR OR PLACE: ______________ 18/

ADDRESS OR DESCRIPTION: ______________

____

CODE LOCATION: In community . . . . 6 — 19/y

Out of community . . 7

SAME DOCTOR OR PLACE AS NAMED IN Q. 6 . (SKIP TO Q. 17). . X

---

13. IF OBVIOUS, CODE WITHOUT ASKING: Is that a private doctor, a hospital clinic or emergency room, a chiropractor, a union or H.I.P doctor, or what?

Private doctor . (ASK A). . . . . . 1 — 20/

Hospital clinic or emergency room 2

Chiropractor. 3

Union or H.I.P. doctor. .(ASK A). . 4

Other . . . (SPECIFY) 5

A. IF PRIVATE, UNION, OR H.I.P. DOCTOR: Is he a general practitioner or some kind of specialist?

General practitioner . . . . . 7 — 21/y

Specialist . . (ASK [1]) . . . 8

Don't know 9

[1] IF SPECIALIST: What kind of specialist is he? — 22/

See Spex for Q. 7.

DECK 01

14. When you get medical help or advice for yourself, how often do you get it from (DOCTOR OR PLACE NAMED IN Q. 12)--some of the time, hardly ever, or never?

(Q. 12-A)

If both a doctor and a place were recorded on the "name" line in Q. 12-A, read only the name of the place here.

Some of the time.	1	23/y
Hardly ever	2	
Never . . . (SKIP TO Q. 17). . .	3	

15. How long does it usually take you to get there (the way you usually go)?

0-9 minutes.	1	24/y
10-19 minutes	2	
20-29 minutes	3	
30-39 minutes	4	
40-49 minutes	5	
50-59 minutes	6	
1 hour or more.	7	

16. Once you get there, about how long do you usually have to wait to see the doctor?

Less than 1/2 hour.	1	25/y
1/2 to less than one hour	2	
One hour to less than 1-1/2 hours	3	
More than 1-1/2 hours	4	
Don't know.	5	

DECK 01

IF RESPONDENT IS 17 YEARS OR OVER, ASK Q. 17.

17. What were you doing most of the past 12 months--

FOR FEMALES . . . keeping house, working or doing something else?

FOR MALES . . . working, or doing something else?

CIRCLE ONE CODE ONLY.

IF "SOMETHING ELSE," PROBE: What were you doing?

If the R. has done two or more different activities in the past 12 months (a woman who kept house and had a job), probe for the one activity R. did most of the time. If the activities took equal amounts of time-- ask for the one she considers her most important activity.

Working	(SKIP TO Q. 19). .	1	26/y
Keeping house	(SKIP TO Q. 19). .	2	
Going to school . . .	(SKIP TO Q. 21). .	3	
Retired	(SKIP TO Q. 20). .	4	
Other . .	(SPECIFY AND SKIP TO Q. 20). .	5	

IF RESPONDENT IS 14 THROUGH 16 YEARS OLD, ASK Q. 18.

18. What were you doing most of the past 12 months--going to school or doing something else?

CIRCLE ONE CODE ONLY.

IF "SOMETHING ELSE," PROBE: What were you doing?

Same as for Q. 17.

Going to school . . .	(SKIP TO Q. 21). .	1	27/y
Working	(GO TO Q. 19). . .	2	
Keeping house	(GO TO Q. 19). . .	3	
Other .	(SPECIFY AND SKIP TO Q. 22). . .	4	

DECK 01

IF "WORKING" OR "KEEPING HOUSE," ASK Q. 19. Read the one appropriate phrase only, (from Q's 17 or 18).

19. In terms of health, are you presently able to (work/keep house) at all?
In this Q. we want to know if any long-term kind of illness or health problem is now keeping the R. from her usual activity (even if the illness or problem began only a short time ago). We are not interested in cases where the R. is home from work temporarily with a short-term kind of illness, such as a toothache, or a cold.

A. IF YES: Are you limited in the kind of (work/housework) you can do, because of your health?
An example of limitation in kind of work: a person can't lift heavy objects, or can't do heavy work, such as scrubbing floors, because of her health.

Yes . (SKIP TO Q. 23). . . .	3	29/y
No. . . . (ASK [1])	4	

[1] IF NO TO A: Are you limited in the amount of (work/housework) you can do, because of your health?
An example of limitation in amount of work: a person can't work full-time, or has to take regular rest periods, because of health.

Yes . (SKIP TO Q. 23). . . .	5	30/y
No. . . . (ASK [2])	6	

[2] IF NO TO [1]: Are you limited in the kind or amount of other activities you can do, because of your health?
Whatever the R. thinks of as being limited.

Yes . (SKIP TO Q. 23). . . .	7	31/y
No. . (SKIP TO Q. 24). . . .	8	

IF "RETIRED," OR "OTHER" IN Q. 17, ASK Q. 20.

20. Does your health keep you from working?

Yes . (SKIP TO Q. 23). . . .	1	32/y
No. . . . (ASK A)	2	

A. IF NO: Are you limited in the kind of work you could do, because of your health?

Yes . (SKIP TO Q. 23). . . .	3	33/y
No. . . . (ASK [1])	4	

[1] IF NO TO A: Are you limited in the amount of work you could do, because of your health?

Yes . (SKIP TO Q. 23). . . .	5	34/y
No. . . . (ASK [2])	6	

[2] IF NO TO [1]: Are you limited in the kind or amount of other activities you can do, because of your health?

Yes . (SKIP TO Q. 23). . . .	7	35/y
No. . (SKIP TO Q. 24). . . .	8	

36-41/R

DECK 01

IF "GOING TO SCHOOL," ASK Q. 21. — (Regardless of age.)

21. Do you have to go to a certain type of school, because of your health?

Yes . (SKIP TO Q. 23). . 1 42/y

No . . . (ASK A) . . 2

A. IF NO: Are you limited in school attendance, because of your health?

Yes . (SKIP TO Q. 23) . 3 43/y

No . . . (ASK [1]) . . 4

[1] IF NO TO A: Are you limited in the kind or amount of other activities you can do, because of your health?

Yes . (SKIP TO Q. 23). . 5 44/y

No . (SKIP TO Q. 24). . 6

IF "OTHER" IN Q. 18, ASK Q. 22. ask only if R. is under 17, and activity was "other."

22. Does your health keep you from going to school?

Yes . (SKIP TO Q. 23). . 1 45/y

No . . . (ASK A) . . . 2

A. IF NO: Would you have to go to a certain type of school, because of your health?

Yes . . (GO TO Q. 23) . 3 46/y

No . . . (ASK [1]) . . 4

[1] IF NO TO A: Would you be limited in school attendance, because of your health?

Yes . . (GO TO Q. 23) . 5 47/y

No . . . (ASK [2]) . . 6

[2] IF NO TO [1]: Are you limited in the kind or amount of other activities you can do, because of your health?

Yes . . (GO TO Q. 23) . 7 48/y

No . (SKIP TO Q. 24) . 8

DECK 01

23. ASK IF ANY LIMITATION BECAUSE OF HEALTH (FROM Q'S. 19, 20, 21, OR 22).

A. What condition causes this? *(circled; handwritten: Refers to the limitation in R's activities.)* RECORD BELOW NAME OF CONDITION OR SYMPTOMS, CAUSES, AND/OR PARTS OF BODY AFFECTED. (IF ANSWER IS "OLD AGE," RECORD VERBATIM AND PROBE: What specific condition causes this limitation?) PROBE, BEFORE GOING ON TO B: Is this limitation caused by any other conditions? (What are they?) PROBE AS ABOVE FOR NAME OR DESCRIPTION OF CONDITION. RECORD EACH CONDITION IN SEPARATE SPACE BELOW AND REPEAT PROBE.	B. ASK FOR EACH CONDITION IN A: Have you had (CONDITION) for more than three months?	C. IF TWO OR MORE CONDITIONS IN A, ASK: Which of these conditions would you say is the main cause of your limitation? CODE ONE CONDITION ONLY.
(a) Record verbatim. (1) *(b) Make sure you get a very clear picture of whatever the condition is. Never accept a vague answer such as "Heart" without probing to find out what is the matter with R's heart.* 49-50/	Yes . 1 No . . 2 51/y	Main cause . 1 52/
(2) *(c) In this question we are asking about any conditions which could be considered long-term (no matter how recently they occurred). We are not concerned with such things as a cold which kept R. out of work for a few days.* 53-54/	Yes . 1 No . . 2 55/y	Main cause . 1 56/
(3) *EXAMPLES* 57-58/	Yes . 1 No . . 2 59/y	Main cause . 1 60/
(1) *Heart. X Well, I have an over-sized heart, and the doctor says I can't exert myself and must take a nap every day. X That's all I know about it.* 61-62/	Yes (1) No . . 2 63/y	Main cause . 1 64/
(2) *Arthritis. X I got bad knees and fingers. X Just got bad a few months ago. I can hardly do anything with my hands now.* 65-66/	Yes . (1) No . . 2 67/y	Main cause (1) *Whatever R. thinks of as the main cause of her activity limitation.* 68/ 69/

BEGIN DECK 02
05-06/00

Read one phrase only --
R's main activity over the last 12 months
(from Q's 17 or 18).

ASK EVERYONE:

24. Thinking back over the last 12 months, that is, since (MONTH), 1967, were you

kept from { going to work, / going to school, / doing your usual activity, } for at least two days in a row, because of an illness or accident?

If R. is female: aside from a normal pregnancy

Yes 1   07/y

No. .(SKIP TO INSTRUCTIONS BEFORE Q. 47, AT TOP OF PAGE 20.) . . . 2

(a) Q. 24 refers to anything at all connected with health which kept R. from doing her usual activity for at least two days in a row -- whether the problem was big or small -- whether it is a long-term or a short-term type of condition.

(b) Give the R. time to think, and encourage her to do so.

(c) If the R. answers "No" to Q. 24, be sure to probe before going on.
A suggested probe to use is: "Are you sure there has been nothing in the past 12 months which kept you from (work/school/ your usual activity) for at least 2 days, whether it was big or small?"

NOTE FOR THE PINK BOOKLETS: In the Pink Booklet there are only two phrases to choose from. You will choose the one to read by the child's major activity during the last 12 months, as you do for the adults. If the child was going to school for most of the time, use the phrase about school -- if anything other than school, use the other phrase.

DECK 02

25. How many different times in the last 12 months were you kept from (work/school/your usual activity) for at least 2 days in a row because of an illness or accident? NOTE: We are not interested in the number of days R. was kept from her activity, but the number of times a health problem stopped R's activity. ______ times 08/

26. ASK Q. 26 FOR EACH TIME MENTIONED IN Q. 25, STARTING WITH THE MOST RECENT TIME.
AFTER ASKING Q. 26 FOR ALL THE TIMES, THEN ASK Q. 26-A FOR EACH CONDITION.

See "Spex Supplement" for further instructions on this question.

(1) The last time this happened, what condition or health problems kept you from (work/school/your usual activity)? RECORD NAME OF CONDITION, OR SYMPTOMS, CAUSES AND/OR PARTS OF BODY AFFECTED. IF MORE THAN ONE CONDITION AT SAME TIME, RECORD ALL IN SAME SPACE.

RECORD VERBATIM 09/

10/

Last month I had tonsillitis -- I was sick for 5-6 days. 11/ 12/

(2) The time before that, what condition or health problems kept you from (work/school/your usual activity)?

16/

I had an asthma attack in the spring. 17/

18/

19/

(3) The time before that, what condition or health problems kept you from (work/school/your usual activity)?

EXAMPLES

I sprained my ankle last spring, too. X No, that was a month before the asthma. 23/ 24/

25/

26/

(4) The time before that, what condition or health problems kept you from (work/school/your usual activity)?

I had another asthma attack last winter. 30/
X That was bad -- I had to miss 3-4 days of work. 31/ 32/

33/

(5) The time before that, what condition or health problems kept you from (work/school/your usual activity)?

I had a bad sore throat last winter. 37/
X That turned out to be tonsillitis, too. 38/

39/

40/

DECK 02

Whenever the word CONDITION is in capital letters you say the name of the condition.

A.	B.
When did you first (notice the CONDITION ~~/have the accident)~~--(~~aside from this particular attack of it)~~? RECORD BEGINNING DATE FOR EACH CONDITION. Don't read this phrase for a non-chronic illness -- such as tonsillitis. Month: Sept. Year: 1968 13-14/	IF NO DATES IN Q. 26-A ARE WITHIN LAST 12 MONTHS, SKIP TO INSTRUCTIONS BEFORE Q. 47, AT TOP OF PAGE 20. IF ANY DATES ARE WITHIN LAST 12 MONTHS, CIRCLE "X" IN BOX ALONGSIDE MOST RECENT DATE. most recent date in last 12 months. X 15/
When did you first (notice the CONDITION~~/have the accident)~~--(aside from this particular attack of it)? Month: I don't remember the month. X summer X D.K. Year: 1943 20-21/	you do read this phrase for asthma -- a chronic (long-term) condition. X 22/
When did you first (~~notice the CONDITION/~~have the accident)~~--(aside from this particular attack of it)~~? Month: April Year: 1968 27-28/	Read this phrase for an injury, such as a sprained ankle. X 29/
When did you first (notice the CONDITION/have the accident)--(aside from this particular attack of it)? Month Year Don't ask this again -- we already have the information for this condition, in 26-A (2), above. 34-35/	X 36/
When did you first (notice the CONDITION~~/have the accident)~~--(~~aside from this particular attack of it)~~? Month: Around Christmas X December Year: 1967 41-42/	X 43/

ASK FOR THE CONDITION CODED "X": Now, let's make sure I have this right--you were kept from (ACTIVITY) for at least two days during the last 12 months because of (CONDITION X); is that correct? (work/school/your usual activity)

IF CORRECT, GO ON TO Q. 27. IF INCORRECT, GO BACK AND CORRECT.

DECK 02

27. Now I'm going to ask you a few questions about (CONDITION "X" FROM Q. 26). When you first (noticed CONDITION/had the accident), at the very beginning, how serious did you think it was--very serious, fairly serious, or not serious at all?

Very serious	1	44/
Fairly serious	2	
Not serious at all . .	3	

28. When you first (noticed CONDITION/had the accident) did you talk to anyone living in the household about what to do about it?

See "Spex Supplement" for further instructions on this question in the Pink Booklet.

Yes . (ASK A & B) . .	4	45/
No	5	

IF YES, ASK A & B:

A. (IF OBVIOUS, CODE WITHOUT ASKING.) Who did you talk to? CODE AS MANY AS APPLY.	B. ASK FOR EACH. What did (PERSON) think you should do?	
Spouse 1		46/
Other person . . . 2		47/
Other person . . . 3		48/

We must ask this question even if the R. is currently living alone (Q. 4)-- because the condition could have occurred anytime in the last 12 months -- and the R. might not have been living alone at that time.

29. When you first (noticed CONDITION/had the accident), did you, or anyone in the household, talk with someone who doesn't live here about what to do about it--a relative; friend or neighbor; a nurse; a druggist; or someone else, not counting a doctor?

Yes . (ASK A & B) . .	1	49/
No	2	

IF YES, ASK A & B:

A. Who was that? CODE AS MANY AS APPLY. READ CATEGORIES, IF NECESSARY.	B. ASK FOR EACH. What did (PERSON) think you should do?	
Relative, friend, or neighbor 3		50/
Nurse 4		51/
Druggist 5		52/
Other person 6		53/
Other person 7		54/

If more than one relative, friend, or neighbor, circle code 3, record the number of people, and record the answer to "B" for each person on a separate line.

DECK 02

30. Did you, or anyone in the household, see or talk to a doctor about your (CONDITION/accident)?

Yes. 1 55/y

No . . (SKIP TO Q. 42). . . . 2

---

31. Was the doctor you saw or spoke to the first time, the doctor you usually go to?

Yes. 3 56/y

No 4

---

32. How soon was it after you first (noticed CONDITION/had the accident) that the doctor was seen, or talked to on the phone? About how many days?

(RECORD NUMBER OF DAYS OR CODE "SAME DAY.") __________ days 57-58/

Same day as first (noticed condition/had accident). 00

---

33. Please look at this card and tell me where that first call or visit was.

HAND CARD A

First saw a doctor at:

Hospital emergency room. 1 59/

Hospital clinic. 2

Clinic not connected with a hospital (including a union or H.I.P. clinic). 3

Private doctor, in his office. 4

Private doctor, in your home 5

First talked on the phone, to a:

Private doctor 6

Union or H.I.P. doctor 7

First saw or talked to a doctor somewhere else (SPECIFY). 8

In this question we are interested in the very first contact with a doctor. If R. called the dr. and he said to come right in -- and R. did -- we still want the telephone call coded here. Consider a telephone call a contact only if a doctor was spoken to -- and not a nurse or receptionist.

IF INFORMATION VOLUNTEERED THAT PERSON WAS KEPT, OR SENT, TO STAY OVERNIGHT IN HOSPITAL AT FIRST CALL OR VISIT, CIRCLE CODE X BELOW.

Went directly to hospital. . (SKIP TO Q. 41). . . . X 60/

---

34. Did the doctor prescribe, or give you, any medicine or shots that first time?

first doctor contact - phone or visit.

Yes 6 61/y

No. 7

IF FIRST CONTACT WITH DOCTOR WAS A PHONE CALL, SKIP TO Q. 36.

35. Did you have any tests or X-rays during that first visit?

Yes 8 62/y

No. 9

DECK 02

Includes first contact by anyone in the household.

36. When (you) talked to the doctor that first time for (CONDITION), did he tell you to (come back/come in)?

Read this if first contact was a visit. Read this if first contact was a phone call.

Yes	.(ASK A) . .	1	63/y
No	. . . .	2	

A. IF YES: Did you?

Yes	. . . .	3	64/y
No	.(ASK [1]). .	4	

[1] IF NO TO A: Why didn't you?

Not time yet . . .	5	65/
Other (SPECIFY). .	6	

---

37. How many times altogether, including that first time, was any doctor seen or talked to about this (condition/accident)?

______________ times 66-67/

First time only . (SKIP TO Q. 40) . . . 01

---

38. Was it the same (doctor/place) every time?

Yes	. . . .	1	68/y
No	. . (ASK A). .	2	

A. IF NO: How did you decide to go to a different (doctor/place)--did the first (doctor/place) send you to the second one, or did you or your family decide to see another doctor, or what?

Read this if first contact was with a private doctor. Read this if first contact was hospital or clinic.

Sent by first doctor . .	3	69/
Own or family decision .	4	
Other (SPECIFY)	5	

---

39. Did you have any (other) tests or X-rays during any visit after the first time for this (condition/accident)?

Use this only if R. got tests or X-rays on first visit (Q. 35)

Yes	. . . .	6	70/y
No	. . . .	7	

---

40. Did any doctor you saw or talked to suggest that you should stay overnight in a hospital for (CONDITION)?

If a doctor said that R. might have to stay overnight, but he didn't know yet-- code as "no."

Yes. .	(ASK A) . .	1	71/y
No	. . . .	2	

A. IF YES: Did you?

Yes	. . . .	3	72/y
No	. (ASK [1]) .	4	

[1] IF NO TO A: Why didn't you?

If answer to "A" is yes, keep this in mind--as you'll be asking about the hospitalization later (in Q's 50-52).

73/

74/

BEGIN DECK 03
05-06/00

41. Do you expect to see or talk to a doctor again about this particular condition?

Yes	5	07/y
No.	6	
Depends	7	

---

42. Did you take any kind of medicine for (CONDITION)?

This refers to anything R. thinks of as medicine -- could include aspirin, home remedies, patent medicine, etc.

Yes . . .(ASK A) . .	1	08/y
No	2	

A. IF YES: Was (any of) this medicine prescribed by a doctor?

Yes	3	09/y
No . . (ASK [1]) . .	4	

[1] IF NO TO A: Was (any of) this medicine bought in a drugstore?

Yes	5	10/y
No	6	

---

43. Thinking about this time when you had (CONDITION), how many days altogether was it that you couldn't (go to work)/(go to school)/(do your usual activity)? PROBE FOR BEST GUESS.

Read one phrase only -- the one you used in Q. 24.

__________ days 11-13/

---

44. About how many of those days did you have to stay in bed, all or most of the day, because of this (condition/accident)? PROBE FOR BEST GUESS.

__________ days 14-16/

---

45. Was this the first time you have had (CONDITION)?

This question should be asked even if the condition was the result of an accident. ("Was this the first time you've had a broken leg?")

Yes	1	17/y
No	2	

---

46. Are you limited in any way in what you can do now, because of this (condition/accident)?

Whatever the R. thinks of as being limited.

Yes	3	18/y
No	4	

DECK 03

IF RESPONDENT IS MALE, SKIP TO Q. 50. IF RESPONDENT IS FEMALE OVER 50 YEARS, SKIP TO Q. 50.

And now a few questions about pregnancy.

47. Are you pregnant now?
If R. says she might be pregnant, but doesn't know yet, code as "no."

Yes	1	19/y
No	2	

---

48. (Besides this pregnancy . .) Have you been pregnant in the last 12 months--that is, since (MONTH), 1967? I'm interested in any pregnancy, even if it ended in a miscarriage.
Use this phrase if R. says she is pregnant now, in Q. 47.

Yes . (ASK A-E)	3	20/y
No . (GO TO Q. 49)	4	

IF YES:

A. How did the pregnancy end--was it a live birth, a miscarriage, or what?

Live birth	5	21/y
Miscarriage	6	
Stillbirth	7	

B. How many months along were you when the pregnancy ended?

Less than three months . . .	1	22/y
3, 4, or 5 months	2	
6 months	3	
7 months	4	
8 months	5	
9 months	6	
10 months	7	

DECK 03

48. (Continued)

C. Did you see a doctor about your pregnancy at any time before (the baby was born/the miscarriage)?

Not including the actual time of the Delivery (or miscarraige).

Yes . (ASK [1] & [2]) 1 23/y

No . (GO TO D) 2

IF YES TO C:

[1] How many times? ____________________visits 24-25/

[2] How many months pregnant were you when you first saw a doctor? ____________________months 26/

D. Did you have a check-up for this pregnancy a month or two after (the baby was born/the miscarriage)?

Yes 1 27/y

No 2

E. IF MISCARRIAGE, DO NOT ASK E: Was the baby delivered by a doctor?

Yes 3 28/y

No 4

DECK 03

IF RESPONDENT IS NOT FEMALE HEAD OF HOUSE, OR WIFE OF HEAD, SKIP TO Q. 50.

49. IF RESPONDENT IS PREGNANT NOW, USE PHRASE (1). IF SHE IS NOT PREGNANT NOW, USE PHRASE (2).

Use phrases in parentheses if R. is currently married.

(1) Before you became pregnant this time, had you (or your husband) been . . .
(2) Are you (or your husband) . . .

. . . using anything or doing anything to keep (you) from getting pregnant?

This could refer to 2 possible situations:
(a) R. (or her husband) was using something, but stopped when she decided to get pregnant -- or
(b) R. (or her husband) was using something, but she got pregnant, anyway.

Yes . (ASK A) 1   29/y

No 2

IF VOLUNTEERED:
Don't need to; not having sexual relations, past menopause, or had operation 3

A. IF YES: (Are/Were) you using the birth control pill, the intrauterine device--that is, loop, coil, spring or bow--or something else?

If more than one method used, probe for the most recent used -- and circle one code only.

Birth control pill . (ASK [1]) . 4   30/y

Intrauterine device (loop, coil, spring, or bow) . (ASK [1]) . . 5

Something else 6

[1] IF USES PILL OR DEVICE: Where do you get (them/it)? (IF MORE THAN ONE PLACE, PROBE: Where did you get [them/it] the last time?) CIRCLE ONE CODE ONLY.

Hospital clinic 1   31/

Other clinic 2

Private doctor 3

Drugstore 4

Other (SPECIFY) 5

DECK 03

ASK EVERYONE: *Hospitalization could have been mentioned in Q.40-A, or the box below Q.33.*

50. (IF HOSPITALIZATION IN LAST 12 MONTHS ALREADY MENTIONED, CODE "YES" TO Q. 50 WITHOUT ASKING, AND GO ON TO 50-A.)

Have you been a patient in a hospital at any time in the last 12 months--since (MONTH), 1967?

This refers to an overnight (or longer) stay in a hospital.

Yes . . (ASK A) . . 1 32/y

No 2

A. IF YES: Altogether, how many different times were you a hospital patient, since (MONTH), 1967?

_____________ times 33/

---

51. Have you been a patient in a nursing home, convalescent home, or any place like that, in the last 12 months--since (MONTH), 1967?

Overnight (or longer) stay.

Yes . . . . . . (ASK A) 1 34/y

No (SKIP TO INSTRUCTION AT BOTTOM OF THIS PAGE) 2

A. IF YES: Altogether, how many different times were you a patient in a nursing home, or any place like that, since (MONTH), 1967?

_____________ times 35/

IF RESPONDENT WAS IN A HOSPITAL, NURSING HOME, OR SIMILAR PLACE IN LAST 12 MONTHS (YES TO Q'S. 50 OR 51), ASK Q. 52, ON NEXT PAGE.

IF NO TO BOTH Q'S. 50 AND 51, SKIP TO Q. 53, ON PAGE 26.

DECK 03

52. ASK A-F ABOUT EACH DIFFERENT STAY IN A HOSPITAL OR NURSING HOME (OR SIMILAR PLACE) IN THE LAST 12 MONTHS. START WITH THE MOST RECENT STAY. ASK A-F FOR EACH STAY BEFORE GOING ON TO THE STAY BEFORE THAT.

I'm going to ask a few questions about the time(s) you were in the hospital (nursing home). (Let's start with the last time.)

Use these phrases if R. has been in hospital or nursing home more than once in past 12 months.

	Most recent stay	Stay before that
A. When did you enter the (hospital/nursing home) (that time)? PROBE FOR MONTH AND YEAR.	Month ____ Year ____ 36-37	Month ____ Year ____ 52-53
B. How many nights were you in the (hospital/nursing home) (that time)?	____ Nights 38-39	____ Nights 54-55
C. What is the name and address of this (hospital/nursing home)? RECORD NAME, ADDRESS OR DESCRIPTION, AND CITY.	Name: ____ Add.: ____ City: ____ 40-41	Name: ____ Add.: ____ City: ____ 56-57
D. For what condition did you enter the (hospital/nursing home)--do you know the medical name? IF NAME NOT KNOWN, PROBE FOR SYMPTOMS, CAUSES, AND/OR PARTS OF BODY AFFECTED.	Probe fully for condition if first response is not clear. 42 43 44 45	58 59 60 61
E. Did you have any operations during this stay at the (hospital/nursing home)?	Yes (ASK [1]&[2] . 1 46/y No 2	Yes(ASK [1]&[2]) . 1 62/y No 2
IF YES TO E: [1] Can you tell me the name, or what kind of operation that was? IF NAME NOT KNOWN, PROBE FOR DESCRIPTION OF WHAT WAS DONE.	If you are asked, a caesarean section is considered an operation. 47 48	63 64
[2] Any other operation (that time)? (IF YES: DESCRIBE.) (Repeat [1] above)	One operation only . 1 Yes, other operation. 2 49 50	One operation only . 1 Yes, other operation 2 65 66

IF HOSPITALIZATION WAS FOR CHILDBIRTH, DO NOT ASK F.

F. Did you see a doctor about (CONDITION) after you got out of the hospital?	Yes . . . . 3 51/y No 4	Yes . . . . 3 67/y No 4

BEGIN DECK 04
05-06/00

Stay before that	Stay before that	Stay before that
______ Month Year 07-08	______ Month Year 23-24	______ Month Year 39-40
______ Nights 09-10	______ Nights 25-26	______ Nights 41-42
Name: ______ Add.: ______ City: ______ 11-12	Name: ______ Add.: ______ City: ______ 27-28	Name: ______ Add.: ______ City: ______ 43-44
13 14 15 16	29 30 31 32	45 46 47 48
Yes (ASK [1]&[2]) . 1 17/y No 2	Yes (ASK [1]&[2]) . 1 33/y No 2	Yes (ASK [1]&[2]) . 1 49/y No 2
18 19	34 35	50 51
One operation only . 1 Yes, other operation 2 20 21	One operation only . 1 Yes, other operation 2 36 37	One operation only . 1 Yes, other operation 2 52 53
Yes . . . . 3 22/y No 4	Yes . . . . 3 38/y No 4	Yes . . . . 3 54/y No 4

DECK 04

ASK EVERYONE: whatever R. considers a general physical check-up.

53. When was the last time you had a general physical check-up? (Just your best guess.)

55-58/

____
(MONTH) (YEAR)

Never had one (SKIP TO Q. 55) . . 0

IF HAD PHYSICAL CHECK-UP WITHIN LAST 12 MONTHS, ASK Q. 54.

54. The last time you had a check-up . . . READ EACH ITEM, AND CIRCLE ONE CODE FOR EACH.

	Yes	No	Don't know	
A. Did anyone take your blood pressure?	4	5	6	59/y
B. Did the doctor have you undress so he could examine your chest and stomach?	7	8	9	60/y
C. Did he test your knee jerk by striking your knee?	1	2	3	61/y
D. Did he examine your rectum?	4	5	6	62/y
E. Did he give you a cardiogram or heart test?	1	2	3	63/y
F. IF RESPONDENT IS FEMALE, ASK: Did he give you an internal or vaginal exam?	4	5	6	64/y

→ Doctor or anyone (as in A), applies to all these.

BEGIN DECK 05
05-06/00

ASK EVERYONE — If R. asks, do not include visits or calls to make appointments or to pay or discuss a bill. We are interested only in visits or calls which concern R's health.

55. About how long has it been since you saw or talked to a medical doctor about your own health--for any kind of condition, even for a few minutes?

_________ months OR _________ years 07-08/

IF MORE THAN 12 MONTHS, SKIP TO Q. 57.

56. Altogether (including the visits we have already talked about), how many times in the last 12 months did you see or talk to a doctor, or go to any of these places, about your own health? First, to a hospital emergency room? . . .
READ EACH CODE CATEGORY, AND RECORD NUMBER OF VISITS TO EACH. RECORD "0" IF NONE.

If you have recorded doctor visits or calls earlier in the interview, read this phrase. All doctor contacts in the last 12 months (including for a check-up) should be summarized here -- (except as a hospital bed-patient).

	# OF CONTACTS	
A. Hospital emergency room		09-10/
B. Hospital out-patient clinic		11-12/
C. Clinic not connected with a hospital ← Includes union and H.I.P. clinics		13-14/
D. Private doctor, in his office		15-16/
E. Talk to a private doctor, over the telephone		17-18/
F. See a private doctor, in your home		19-20/
G. Did you go anywhere else to see a doctor (not counting visits by a doctor while you were a patient in a hospital)? (IF YES, SPECIFY.)		21-22/
Total Contacts:		23-25/

That's a total of _________ visits and calls in the last 12 months--does that sound right? (IF NOT RIGHT, GO OVER CATEGORIES WITH RESPONDENT.)

57. Altogether during the last 12 months, how many days did you have to stay in bed, all or most of the day, because of illness or injury?

Total bed days in past 12 months. _____________ days 26-28/

DECK 05

IF RESPONDENT IS 65 OR OVER, ASK Q. 58.

58. Do you have a Medicare card?

If "no" go on to the next question.

Yes. . . .(ASK A). . .	1	29/y
No	(2)	

A. IF YES: It would be helpful if I could see your Medicare card to find out about the coverage--may I see it?

CODE TYPE(S) OF COVERAGE FROM CARD, OR CIRCLE APPROPRIATE "NO CARD SHOWN" CODE.

From Card:

Hospital coverage	3	30/y
Doctor (Medical) coverage	4	
No coverage shown (ASK [1])	(5)	

"No Card Shown":

Can't locate card (ASK [1])	(6)	
Refused . . . . . (ASK [1])	(7)	

[1] IF NO COVERAGE SHOWN, OR "NO CARD SHOWN" (CODES 5, 6, OR 7 CIRCLED IN A):

Are you covered by that part of Medicare that pays for doctor's bills--that is, the Medicare plan for which you (or some agency) must pay $4.00 a month?

Yes	4	31/y
No.	5	
Don't know. . .	6	

IF RESPONDENT IS MALE, 17 YEARS OR OVER, ASK Q. 59

59. I'm going to read a list of reasons people sometimes give for not seeing a medical doctor when perhaps they should. Please tell me, for each of these reasons, whether or not it has ever kept you from seeing a doctor. . . READ ITEMS, AND CIRCLE ONE CODE FOR EACH.

	Yes	No	Don't Know	Doesn't Apply; Never Worked	
A. You didn't want to lose time or pay from work? (Did that ever keep you from seeing a doctor when perhaps you should have?).	1	2	3	4	32/y
B. You were worried that your boss might think you were too sick to work. . .	5	6	7	8	33/y
C. You didn't think a doctor could help you? (Did that ever keep you from seeing a doctor when perhaps you should have?).	1	2	3	-	34/y
D. The doctor or place didn't have office hours that were convenient for you?	4	5	6	-	35/y

DECK 05

ASK EVERYONE

60. About how long has it been since you were last treated or examined by a dentist?

_________ months or _________ years 36-37/

Never X

IF WITHIN LAST 12 MONTHS, ASK A-D:

A. How many times have you been to a dentist in the last 12 months?

_________ visits 38-39/

B. When you last saw a dentist, was it for an emergency visit?

Yes 7 40/y

No 8

C. What have you had done by a dentist or assistant during the last 12 months? First, have you had your teeth checked, X-rayed or cleaned?

READ EACH ITEM, AND CODE "YES" OR "NO" FOR EACH.

	Yes	No	
(1) Teeth checked, X-rayed, or cleaned . . .	1	2	41/y
(2) Teeth fixed or filled	3	4	42/y
(3) Bridgework repaired	5	6	43/y
(4) Teeth or bridgework replaced	7	8	44/y
(5) Tooth or teeth pulled	1	2	45/y
(6) Any other work? (SPECIFY)	3	4	46/y

D. How long does it usually take you to get to the dentist? (The way you usually go.)

0-9 minutes 1 47/y
10-19 minutes 2
20-29 minutes 3
30-39 minutes 4
40-49 minutes 5
50-59 minutes 6
1 hour or more 7
Sees school dentist . . 8

DECK 05

Now just a few background questions.

61. What is the highest grade or year you completed in school?

If R. received schooling in another country, where the grade system is different from ours, ask R. to guess which of our code categories comes closest to the amount of schooling she had.

No schooling	01	48-49/yy
1st to 2nd grade	02	
3rd to 4th grade	03	
5th to 7th grade	04	
8th grade	05	
9th grade	06	
High school, incomplete (grades 10 or 11)	07	
High school, incomplete--plus vocational or business school	08	
High school, complete (12th grade) . . .	09	
Vocational or business school, in addition to completing high school . .	10	
College, incomplete	11	
College, complete	12	
Don't know	13	

---

62. IF OBVIOUS, CODE WITHOUT ASKING. Are you currently married, widowed, divorced, separated, or have you never been married?

From Q.4, or from comments made during the interview.

Married	1	50/y
Widowed	2	
Divorced	3	
Separated	4	
Never married	5	

DECK 05

IF RESPONDENT WAS "KEEPING HOUSE" OR "GOING TO SCHOOL" FOR MOST OF LAST 12 MONTHS (FROM Q's 17 OR 18), SKIP TO Q. 64.

ALL OTHERS, ASK Q. 63.

3. A. What kind of work do you (did you normally) do?

51-53/

(PROBE, IF VAGUE: What do (did) you actually do on that job?)

It is important to get very clear, very specific answers to this question. If you are at all in doubt about the answer R. gives you, use the probes.

B. What kind of business or industry is that?

54-55/

(PROBE, IF VAGUE: What does that (firm/organization/agency) make or do?)

END OF INDIVIDUAL SECTION

56-57/R

BEGIN DECK 07
05-06/RF

64. A. In what state (or country, if outside the U.S.) was (HEAD) born?

STATE: ______________________________ 07-08/

OR

COUNTRY: ______________________________ 09/

IF WIFE OF HEAD LIVING IN HOUSEHOLD, ASK:

B. In what state (or country, if outside the U.S.) was (WIFE OF HEAD) born?

STATE: ______________________________ 10-11/

OR

COUNTRY: ______________________________ 12/

---

65. A. Up to the age of 16, did (HEAD) live mostly on a farm or out in the country, in a village or small town, or in a city, or its suburbs?

Farm or country . . . . 1 — 13
Village or small town . 2
City 3
Suburb of city 4

IF WIFE OF HEAD LIVING IN HOUSEHOLD, ASK:

B. Up to the age of 16, did (WIFE OF HEAD) live mostly on a farm or out in the country, in a village or small town, or in a city, or its suburbs?

Farm or country . . . . 5 — 14
Village or small town . 6
City 7
Suburb of city 8

DECK 07

Now a few more questions about health matters, this time about the whole family.

66. In the last 12 months, has any kind of nurse or health aide come to visit anyone in the household, for any reason? For example, a public health or school nurse, a visiting or home nurse, or some other kind of nurse or health aide?

Yes .(ASK A-C) . . 1 15/y

No 2

IF YES:

A. How many times altogether did a nurse or health aide come here, in the last 12 months?

_______ times 16-17/

B. What kind of nurse (was she/were they)--visiting or home nurse, public health or school nurse, health aide, or what? PROBE FOR BEST GUESS. CODE AS MANY AS APPLY.

Visiting or home nurse 5 18/y

Public health or school nurse 6 19/y

Health aide 8 21/y

Other (SPECIFY) 9 22/y

C. Who did the nurse(s) or health aide(s) come to see? CIRCLE ONE CODE.

One or more adults in household . . . 1 23/y

One or more children in household . . 2

Both adult(s) and child(ren) 3

---

67. Thinking back over the last 12 months, have you--or anyone in the household--seen or talked to a spiritualist, faith healer, or anyone like that, about your--or their--health?

Yes . . (ASK A) . . . 5 24/y

No. 6

A. IF YES: How many times?

_______ times 25/

If R. asks what these are, don't try to explain. Say, "There are people who call themselves spiritualists, or faith healers, and sometimes people go to them for advice. Have you, or anyone in the household ... (REPEAT THE QUESTION)?"

DECK 07

This was formerly the Welfare Dept.

68. Have you, or anyone in the household, been enrolled in Medicaid any time in the last 12 months? (Medicaid is a medical assistance program, which is handled through the New York City Department of Social Services.)

Read this phrase if R. does not seem to know what Medicaid is. If she still doesn't know, record that answer verbatim and circle the "no" code.

Yes	1	26/y
No . (SKIP TO Q. 72)	2	

69. Who has been covered by Medicaid in the last 12 months? (CODE AS MANY AS APPLY.)

Head of household	3	27/y
Spouse of Head	4	28/y
All children of Head in household	5	29/y
Some children of Head in household (SPECIFY WHO)	6	30/y
Other persons in household, <u>related</u> to Head (SPECIFY WHO) . .	7	31/y
Other persons in household, <u>not</u> related to Head (SPECIFY WHO)	8	32/y

70. Is there anyone who <u>has been</u> covered by Medicaid in the last 12 months who is <u>not</u> covered now?

Yes. (ASK A) .	1	33/y
No	2	

A. <u>IF YES</u>: Who is that? (CODE AS MANY AS APPLY.)

Head of household	3	34/y
Spouse of Head	4	35/y
All children of Head in household	5	36/y
Some children of Head in household (SPECIFY WHO)	6	37/y
Other persons in household, <u>related</u> to Head (SPECIFY WHO) . .	7	38/y
Other persons in household, <u>not</u> related to Head (SPECIFY WHO)	8	39/y

71. Who has <u>used</u> Medicaid in the last 12 months? (CODE AS MANY AS APPLY.)

Head of household	3	40/y
Spouse of Head	4	41/y
All children of Head in household	5	42/y
Some children of Head in household (SPECIFY WHO)	6	43/y
Other persons in household, related to Head (SPECIFY WHO) . .	7	44/y
Other persons in household, <u>not</u> related to Head (SPECIFY WHO)	8	45/y
No one	9	46/y

DECK 07

ASK EVERYONE: Use this phrase if the R. is enrolled in Medicare, or anyone in the household is--or has been--enrolled in Medicaid.

72. (Not counting Medicare or Medicaid) . . . Does any member of this household have any insurance that pays all or part of the medical bills when they go to the hospital or doctor--such as Blue Cross/Blue Shield, a commercial plan, a union plan, or some other plan?

Yes.	1	47/y
No .(SKIP TO Q.80) .	2	

48/R

73. Does this insurance pay for just hospital bills, just doctor bills, or both hospital and doctor bills?

If more than one plan in household, code the combined coverage of all the plans.

Hospital only	1	49/y
Doctor only	2	
Both	3	

74. What is the name of the insurance plan? (Any others?)

The name of the plan is usually the name of the insurance company -- such as, Blue Cross, Aetna, Metropolitan, etc.

50/
51/
52/
53/
54/

75. Who is covered by the plan(s)?
(CODE AS MANY AS APPLY.)

Head of household	3	55/y
Spouse of Head	4	56/y
All children of Head in household . .	5	57/y
Some children of Head in household (SPECIFY WHO)	6	58/y
Other persons in household, related to Head (SPECIFY WHO)	7	59/y
Other persons in household, not related to Head (SPECIFY WHO) . . .	8	60/y

76. (Was this insurance plan) (Were these insurance plans) gotten through an employer, a union, directly from a salesman, or what? (CODE AS MANY AS APPLY.)

If more than one plan.

Employer	1	61/y
Union.	3	
Salesman	5	
Other (SPECIFY). .	6	

Q's 77-79 OMITTED

62-66/R

BEGIN DECK 08

05-06/RR

ASK EVERYONE:

Now I would like to ask you a few questions about this (apartment/house).

80. A. How many rooms are there in this (apartment/house)?--Count the kitchen, but not the bathrooms (or unlived in attics and basements).

Read this phrase only if D.U. is a house.

____________ rooms 07-08/

B. And how many of these rooms do people sleep in?

____________ sleeping rooms 09/

IF OBVIOUS, CODE C WITHOUT ASKING:

C. Do you own or rent this (apartment/house)?

Refers to any member of the household.

Own (including still buying) . . .	1	10/y
Rent	2	

---

81. IF THIS D.U. IS AN APARTMENT, ASK Q. 81. IF IT IS A PRIVATE HOUSE, SKIP TO Q. 82.

	Yes	No	
A. Do you have a bathroom, with toilet and bath, in this apartment?	3	4	11/y
B. Do you have any roaches in the apartment?	5	6	12/y
C. Do you have any rats in this building?	7	8	13/y

DECK 08

82. We would like to get an idea of how much money people get from different places.
See "Spex Supplement" for further instructions on this question.

IF ANY PERSONS IN HOUSEHOLD, AGE 17 OR OVER, ARE NOT RELATED TO THE HEAD OR HEAD'S WIFE, READ THIS:
Refers to both Q's 82 and 83.
These questions are just for the family members, so do not include any income that (UNRELATED PERSON[S]) get(s). 14-18/R

A. How much is being earned, altogether, each week, by everyone in the household, from jobs--wages or salary--before taxes? (ENTER TOTAL WEEKLY WAGES, OR CIRCLE "0"; THEN ASK [1].)

Be sure to record weekly amount here.

$______ Weekly 19-22/
None . . . 0

If R. doesn't know exact figures, ask for her best guess and record as an estimate (est.)

[1] Would you say this figure is higher, about the same, or lower than your usual weekly income over the last 12 months?

If R. only knows wages after taxes ("take-home pay"), record that figure, and record that it is "after taxes."

Higher 1
About same . . 2
Lower 3

23/y

Refers to total figure, for everyone in household.

B. Does anyone in the household get any income from Welfare?
(IF YES: How much money does that come to altogether, each month?) (ENTER TOTAL MONTHLY AMOUNT, OR CIRCLE "0")

$______ Monthly 24-27/
None . . . 0

Be sure to record monthly amount here, and in all places below.

C. How much money, if any, does everyone in the household get, altogether, each month, from the following sources:

[1] Social Security or other retirement payments or pensions?
(ENTER TOTAL MONTHLY AMOUNT, OR CIRCLE "0")

$______ Monthly 28-31/
None . . . 0

[2] V.A. payments or Armed Forces allotments?
(ENTER TOTAL MONTHLY AMOUNT, OR CIRCLE "0")

$______ Monthly 32-35/
None . . . 0

[3] Interest, or rental payments? (IF "UNRELATED ADULTS" IN HOUSEHOLD: Including any money that (UNRELATED PERSON[S] may pay to the family?)
(ENTER TOTAL MONTHLY AMOUNT, OR CIRCLE "0")

$______ Monthly 36-39/
None . . . 0

[4] Any other sources, such as child support payments, gifts from outside the household, or anything else?
(ENTER TOTAL MONTHLY AMOUNT, OR CIRCLE "0")

$______ Monthly 40-43/
None . . . 0

Remember: The frame of reference for Q. 82 is the present time-- In A, the present week; In B & C, the present month.

DECK 08

83. Which of these groups on this card includes your total household income during last year--1967? That is, all income, from any sources, before taxes. Just tell me the letter for the amount that fits.

HAND CARD B

If R. can't answer this, ask if she could find out from someone else in the household (her husband, if he is present). If this is not possible, ask for her best guess, and code that, with "est." to show it is her estimate.

A.	$ 0 - $ 499	00	44-45/yy
B.	500 - 999	01	
C.	1,000 - 1,499	02	
D.	1,500 - 1,999	03	
E.	2,000 - 2,499	04	
F.	2,500 - 2,999	05	
G.	3,000 - 3,499	06	
H.	3,500 - 3,999	07	
I.	4,000 - 4,499	08	
J.	4,500 - 4,999	09	
K.	5,000 - 5,999	10	
L.	6,000 - 6,999	11	
M.	7,000 - 7,999	12	
N.	8,000 - 8,999	13	
O.	9,000 - 9,999	14	
P.	10,000 and over	15	
	Don't know	99	
	Refused	xx	

Q. 84. OMITTED 46/R

DECK 08

85. May I have your telephone number, in case my office wants to vertify this interview? (IF NO PHONE, ASK IF THERE IS A PHONE RESPONDENT CAN BE REACHED AT.)

Telephone number: ________________	. . . .	4	47/y
	No phone. . . .	5	
	Refused	6	

IF PHONE NUMBER GIVEN, CODE: PHONE LOCATED IN . . .

Respondent's home. . . .	7	48/
Home of neighbor	8	
Other (SPECIFY).	9	

86. Had you heard of the Red Hook Neighborhood Health Center, before this survey?

Yes	1	49/y
No.	2	

NOW GO TO BLUE OR PINK BOOKLET FOR NEXT PERSON LISTED (IF ANY).

IF NO OTHER PERSONS IN HOUSEHOLD, ASK QUESTION ON YELLOW SHEET.

RECORD TIME: ____________ AM PM

Use this phrase only when you have completed entire interview in household.

(Thank you very much for your time and cooperation. You have been very helpful.)

INTERVIEWER: FILL IN ITEMS BELOW AND ON NEXT PAGE, AFTER YOU LEAVE THE HOUSEHOLD.

BEGIN DECK 09
05-06/RR

INTERVIEWER REMARKS

A. Total length of interview (including supplements done at time of main questionnaire).

__________Minutes 07-09/

B. Respondent's race:

White	1	10/y
Negro	2	
Oriental.	3	
Other (SPECIFY)	4	

C. CODE ALL LANGUAGES SPOKEN IN HOUSEHOLD:

English only.	5	11/y
English and other (ANSWER [1]).	6	
Other only (ANSWER [1]).	7	

[1] IF OTHER: What other language(s)? 12/ 13/ 14/

D. Is respondent Cuban, Puerto Rican, Mexican-American, or American Indian?

Yes, Cuban.	1	15/y
Yes, Puerto Rican . . .	2	
Yes, Mexican-American .	3	
Yes, American Indian. .	4	
No.	6	

INTERVIEWER REMARKS--Continued

DECK 09

E. Is this household in public housing?

Yes	5	16/y
No.	6	

F. CODE TYPE OF STRUCTURE IN WHICH HOUSEHOLD IS LOCATED:

Single-family house, detached.	1	17/
Two-family house, semi-attached, or attached (row) house	2	
Apartment in apartment building.	3	
Apartment in partly business building . . .	4	
Rooming house	5	
Non-transient hotel/motel, etc.	6	
Mobile home (trailer) . .	7	
Other (SPECIFY)	8	

G. RATE THE CONDITION OF THE WALLS IN THIS DWELLING UNIT:

Clean, painted.	1	18/y
Dirty but intact.	2	
Fairly large cracks . . .	3	
Holes in the walls or ceilings.	4	

H, I, J OMITTED 19-29/R

K. In what room(s) of the house was the interview conducted?

30/

31/

L. Everything considered, do you think the respondent enjoyed the interview a great deal, somewhat, not very much, or not at all?

A great deal.	1	32/y
Somewhat.	2	
Not very much	3	
Not at all.	4	

M. Date of interview:

Month	Date	33-36/

N. Interviewer Number:

			37-39/

O. Interviewer Signature:

____

National Opinion Research Center
University of Chicago

NORC
4055
10/68

Red Hook Neighborhood Health Center Survey

QUESTION-BY-QUESTION SPECIFICATIONS SUPPLEMENT

GENERAL INFORMATION

THE QUESTIONNAIRES: The interview is made up of three separate questionnaires: the Main Questionnaire is white. In it are questions about the whole household, and a set of health questions that are about the respondent only.

The Blue Booklet contains the same set of health questions; one of these booklets is to be used to get health information about each other person (besides your respondent) in the household, who is 14 years or older.

The Pink Booklet contains most of the same questions; one of these is to be used for each child in the household under 14. Some of the questions have been omitted for the Pink Booklet, as not being appropriate for children.

In addition, a Yellow Sheet is also part of this interview. It has just one question; it is to be asked of one person only, preferably your respondent on the Main Questionnaire. If that respondent is not available when you have completed all the questionnaires in the household, you may ask the question on the Yellow Sheet of some other adult in the household who is available.

Therefore, if you have a household that contains, say, six persons, you will use: a Main Quex, five of the Blue and/or Pink Booklets--depending on the age of the household members--and one Yellow Sheet.

MORE ABOUT THE BLUE BOOKLETS: You'll note that the questions in the Blue Booklets are almost the same as Q's 5-63 of the Main Quex. They are different only in that the questions in the Blue Booklet are directed to the respondent about another person, so that it uses the terms "he" or "she" instead of "you." Wherever the word (PERSON) appears in parentheses, you should read the name of the person being asked about.

If you come across a household in which some person, who is 17 years or older, is not related to the head or the head's wife, you will have to interview that person about himself/herself; therefore, you will have to change the wording to suit the situation--that is, you will say "you" instead of "he," or "she," or the person's name.

MORE ABOUT THE PINK BOOKLETS: The Pink Booklets, for children under 14, are somewhat different. We want mostly the same information, but there are two important differences:

(1) Some questions are omitted, because they do not apply to young children.

(2) In the questions about doctors seen or talked to, we have to find out not only whether the child himself saw a doctor in a particular situation, but also whether anyone in the household saw, or spoke to, a doctor about the child. That is why some of the questions had to be worded differently for children, and why it was decided to make a different booklet for them.

ABOUT THESE SPECIFICATIONS: Since, in most cases, your respondent will be a woman, we will refer to the respondent as "she" in these Spex to save space--but, of course, the instructions apply to male respondents, as well as female. We will also use the letter "R" to refer to "respondent" in the Spex, as well as in the same places on the questionnaire itself.

QUESTION-BY-SPECIFICATIONS

Q. 4: HOW TO DETERMINE WHO IS THE HEAD OF THE HOUSEHOLD

In most cases you will be able to determine this easily from the information you have gathered about the household already --who is living there and how they are related. In some cases you may have to ask for additional information in order to determine who is Head. Here are rules to follow in determining the Head.

A. HOUSEHOLDS MADE UP OF A HUSBAND AND WIFE--WITHOUT CHILDREN, OR WITH CHILDREN UNDER 21. The husband is the Head.

B. HOUSEHOLDS WHERE THERE IS ONE ADULT (PERSON OVER 21), WITH OR WITHOUT CHILDREN (OR OTHER PERSONS) UNDER 21. The adult is the Head, male or female.

C. HOUSEHOLDS WITH OTHER COMBINATIONS OF ADULTS (WITH OR WITHOUT CHILDREN [OR OTHER PERSONS] UNDER 21).

There can be many combinations in this category; to give a a few examples:

--married children living with a parent or both parents;

--single adult children living with a parent or parents;

--two sisters or brothers sharing a house or apartment;

--two or more friends sharing a house or apartment;

--two or more couples, related or not, sharing a house or apartment.

In all such cases there are a few simple rules to apply:

(1) First, find out if the dwelling unit (house or apartment) was owned or rented by one of the persons (or couples)

first, and the other person(s) or couples moved in with them. In such a case, it is always the person or couple who had the place first (who were "moved in on") who is the Head. (If it is a couple, the husband is the Head. If it is a single person, that person is the Head, male or female.)

ONE EXCEPTION: The only exception to the above rule is if an adult child (or married children) moved in with older parents because one or both parents were too sick, feeble, or senile to take care of themselves. In this case the child or children would be the Head (the husband of the younger couple, if there is a husband).

(2) If all adults in the household moved in at the same time (no one "moved in on" the other), the Head would be the eldest male in the household. If no adult male is living in the household, then the eldest female.

NOTE ONE: If there is no one in the household over 21--use the same rules as above, but ignoring the "over 21" age restriction.

NOTE TWO: If a respondent includes a common-law husband or a boyfriend as a permanent member of the household, consider him as you would a legal husband, when deciding who is the Head.

IF YOU CANNOT DETERMINE "HEAD" BY THE ABOVE RULES: If you have tried to apply the rules given here, but are unable to decide who the Head is because of some special situation, or you cannot get all the information you need, then ASK THE RESPONDENT WHO IS CONSIDERED THE HEAD OF THE HOUSEHOLD, and use that.

Q. 6: Be sure to enter the name of the doctor or place the R. gives you. Try to get as full a name or title as you can.

If the R. says she goes to more than one doctor or place for different things, probe: "Where do you go for general medical care most of the time?"

If the person has recently moved to this community or city, and says she has not been to any doctor here, ask for the doctor or place she has been going to (most of the time), even if it is somewhere else.

Howver, if she has moved here recently, and has been to a doctor or place here at least once--ask if she expects to use that doctor most of the time. If so, record that doctor or place in Q. 6.

Q. 8: The "last 12 months" refers to the time period between this month and this month a year ago. This time period appears many times in the questionnaire.

Q. 12: For some people there is a particular doctor or place that they especially trust more than any other place (even though they may never have been to that doctor or place). For other people, there is no such doctor or place. We are especially interested in finding out how this person feels about this and we want her first reaction. So ask the question clearly and distinctly, and take whatever her first answer is; do not probe.

Q. 12A: If the answer to Q. 12A is the same doctor or place as you were told about in Q. 6, you can skip Q's. 13-16, because they get information you already got in Q's. 7-11.

NOTE ON PINK/BLUE FOR Q'S. 6 & 12: When you get to the Blue and Pink Booklets, you also skip Q's. 7-11 and/or Q's. 13-16 if the doctor or place was named in any of the other booklets or the Main Questionnaire--for this household. This will save you even more time, and we will still have the information on the doctor or place from other parts of the interview in the household.

Q. 26: In 26 we want to know what the health problems are that kept the R. from doing her usual activity, for each time it happened in the last 12 months.

If the R. had more than one health problem at a time, record both of them in the same space. For example, if the R. could not go to work for two weeks in June, 1968, because she had a bad cold which became complicated by the flu, record both of these health problems in the same space.

This is a very important question. Take your time with it and make sure that the R. has thought of everything before you go on to Q. 26A.

Record the R's verbatim responses to this question, and probe, if necessary, to get clear names or descriptions of conditions.

Q. 26A: CHRONIC CONDITIONS: Use the phrase "aside from this particular attack" only when the R's problem is the result of a chronic, or long-term, condition. For example: if the R. had an asthma attack in the last 12 months, you would read 26A as: "When did you first notice the asthma--aside from this particular attack of it?"

NOTE: If, in Q. 26, the R. tells you of two or more attacks of the same chronic condition within the last 12 months, ask Q. 26A only once for that condition--that is, the date on which the R. first noticed the condition. Therefore, you do not get the date of each attack, but just the date on which the condition was first noticed--which may or may not have been within the last 12 months. (See the example in the Question-by-Question Spex.)

If you are not sure whether a certain condition is a chronic condition, treat it as not chronic, and ask for each time it occurred.

TWO OR MORE PROBLEMS AT THE SAME TIME: If the R. mentions two health problems during one episode (as the example mentioned earlier, of the cold which turned into the flu), ask for and record the dates (if they are different) so anyone can tell which date goes with which condition. You may number the conditions and the dates to match ("condition #1" and "date #1"); or you may draw arrows from the condition to its date.

Q. 26B: If any of the dates you have recorded are within the last 12 months, look for the most recent date and circle the "X" in the box next to that date. That becomes "Condition X"--the condition you will be asking about in Q's. 27 through 46.

CHRONIC CONDITIONS: If the R. has a chronic condition, such as high blood pressure, which resulted in two or more attacks during the past 12 months, you will have recorded only one date for it in 26A--the date on which the heart condition was first noticed. If that date was within the last 12 months (and if it is the most recent date you have recorded for this respondent in 26A), then "Condition X," which you will be asking about, is the high blood pressure --when the respondent first noticed it. So that means you are not asking about the R's most recent attack of high blood pressure, but the time when she first noticed her high blood pressure.

It is important that you and the respondent both understand the condition and the time you are talking about when you ask Q's. 27 through 46.

Q. 28: When you are using the Pink Booklet, you will have a choice of the phrases "you" or "(CHILD'S) mother." If your R. is the child's mother, you will use the phrase "you." If your R. is someone else, but the child's mother is living in the household, use the phrase "(CHILD'S) mother." If the mother is not living in the household, use "you," as your R. is probably the person responsible for the care of the child.

In 28A, also in the Pink Booklet, the answer category "Spouse" refers to either the spouse of the respondent, if you used the phrase "you" in Q. 28, or the spouse of the child's mother, if you used the phrase "(CHILD'S) mother" in Q. 28.

INCOME QUESTIONS--Q'S. 82 & 83: If the R. is reluctant to give you income information--appears uncomfortable or refuses--assure her that everything she tells you is strictly confidential and that the information is used for statistical purposes only. It is never connected with her or her family.

Note that we want the total amounts for all members of the household related to the Head or his wife. Be sure to read the full question in each category (A, B, & C) and that the R. knows the kind of income you are asking about in each before you record her answer and go on to the next category.

You may have to do some figuring when you get the income information before you record the totals on page 37. For example, in Q. 82A we ask for weekly wages or salary earned by people in the family. If there is one person working, and he gets paid once a month, you may want to write down his monthly salary and divide by four to get the weekly salary.

Another example of the figuring you may have to do: If there are three people in the household working and earning wages, you may have to write down all their weekly salaries and add them up in order to get the total weekly wages for the family.

If you don't have room to do this figuring on page 37, use extra paper (which you should always carry with you), and enclose the paper with the completed interview when you turn in that case.

END OF MAIN QUESTIONNAIRE: Be sure to fill in the time when you finish the Main Questionnaire. The "interviewer remarks" should be completed as soon as possible after you have left the household. If you have to return to the household later to complete any additional Blue or Pink Booklets, do not wait until you have finished all that before you complete the remarks section; do it as soon as possible after the Main Questionnaire is done, while it is fresh in your mind and not confused with other interviews. But, never do it while you are in the household.

END OF PINK/BLUE BOOKLETS AND YELLOW SHEET: You'll note that the Pink and Blue Booklets (and the Yellow Sheet) all have places on the last page for you to enter your name, the date completed, and to identify your respondent for that particular booklet. If you have time to do this while you are in the household (if you have to wait for an R.), it would be a good idea to fill in the information right away. But don't keep the R. waiting to do it. Do, however, try to do it as soon as possible after you leave the household. If you don't get a chance right away, be sure to do it later when you are looking over the questionnaires and editing them.

CONFIDENTIAL
4055
9/68

Approved through-June 30, 1969

Form approved.
Budget Bureau No. 116-R0146

NATIONAL OPINION RESEARCH CENTER
University of Chicago

OFFICE OF ECONOMIC OPPORTUNITY

NEIGHBORHOOD HEALTH CENTER SURVEY

"BLUE BOOKLET"--FOR PERSONS
IN HOUSEHOLD AGE 14 AND OVER

SEGMENT # ____________ PERSON'S NAME: ______________________________

DULS LINE # ____________ PERSON'S #: ______________________________

Now, we need the same kind of information about (PERSON).

5. In general, would you say (PERSON'S) health is excellent, good, fair, or poor?

Excellent 1
Good 2
Fair 3
Poor 4
Don't know 5

6. Who does (PERSON) see, or where does (he/she) go, most of the time when (he/she) wants to see a doctor for (himself/herself)--to what doctor or place?

NAME OF
DOCTOR OR PLACE: ______________________________

ADDRESS OR
DESCRIPTION: ______________________________

____

CODE LOCATION: In community 6
Out of community . . . 7

SAME DOCTOR OR PLACE AS NAMED FOR ANY OTHER HOUSEHOLD MEMBER . . . . (SKIP TO Q. 12) X

Never goes anywhere (SKIP TO Q. 12) . . 8

7. <u>IF OBVIOUS, CODE WITHOUT ASKING</u>: Is that a private doctor, a hospital clinic or emergency room, a chiropractor, a union or H.I.P. doctor or what?

Private doctor . . . . (ASK A) 1
Hospital clinic or emergency room . . . 2
Chiropractor 3
Union or H.I.P. doctor . . (ASK A) . . 4
Other (SPECIFY) 5

B. <u>IF PRIVATE, UNION, OR H.I.P. DOCTOR</u>: Is he a general practitioner or some kind of specialist?

General practitioner 7
Specialist . . . . . (ASK [1]) 8
Don't know 9

[1] <u>IF SPECIALIST</u>: What kind of specialist is he?

---

8. When did (PERSON) first start going to (DOCTOR OR PLACE NAMED IN Q. 6)--within the last 12 months or longer ago than that?

Within last 12 months 1
Longer ago that that 2

---

9. OMITTED

---

10. How long does it usually take (PERSON) to get there (the way [he/she] usually goes)?

0-9 minutes 1
10-19 minutes 2
20-29 minutes 3
30-39 minutes 4
40-49 minutes 5
50-59 minutes 6
1 hour or more 7
Never went from this address 8
Never went . . . (SKIP TO Q. 12) . . . 9

---

11. Once (PERSON) gets there, about how long does (he/she) usually have to wait to see the doctor?

Less than 1/2 hour 1
1/2 to less than one hour 2
One to less than 1-1/2 hours 3
More than 1-1/2 hours 4

12. Of all the doctors and places (PERSON) knows of, when something worries (him/her) about (his/her) own health, is there any one doctor or place that (he/she) trusts more than any other, to get medical help or advice? (DO NOT PROBE.)

Yes . . . . (ASK A) 1
No . . . . . . (SKIP TO Q. 17) 2

A. IF YES: What doctor or place?

NAME OF DOCTOR OR PLACE: ____________________

ADDRESS OR DESCRIPTION: ____________________

____

CODE LOCATION: In community 1
Out of community . . . 2

SAME DOCTOR OR PLACE AS NAMED IN Q. 6, OR FOR ANY OTHER HOUSEHOLD MEMBER . . . . (SKIP TO Q. 17) X

---

13. IF OBVIOUS, CODE WITHOUT ASKING: Is that a private doctor, a hospital clinic or emergency room, a chiropractor, a union or H.I.P. doctor or what?

Private doctor . . . . (ASK A) 1
Hospital clinic or emergency room . . . 2
Chiropractor 3
Union or H.I.P. doctor . . (ASK A) . . 4
Other . . . . . . (SPECIFY) 5

A. IF PRIVATE, UNION, OR H.I.P. DOCTOR: Is he a general practitioner or some kind of specialist?

General practitioner 7
Specialist . . . . . (ASK [1]) 8
Don't know 9

[1] IF SPECIALIST: What kind of specialist is he?

14. When (PERSON) gets medical help or advice for (himself/herself), how often does (he/she) get it from (DOCTOR OR PLACE NAMED IN Q. 12)--some of the time, hardly ever, or never?

Some of the time 1

Hardly ever 2

Never . . . . . (SKIP TO Q. 17) 3

---

15. How long does it usually take (PERSON) to get there (the way [he/she] usually goes)?

0-9 minutes 1

10-19 minutes 2

20-29 minutes 3

30-39 minutes 4

40-49 minutes 5

50-59 minutes 6

1 hour or more 7

---

16. Once (he/she) gets there, about how long does (he/she) usually have to wait to see the doctor?

Less than 1/2 hour 1

1/2 to less than one hour 2

One hour to less than 1-1/2 hours 3

More than 1-1/2 hours 4

Don't know 5

IF PERSON IS 17 YEARS OR OVER, ASK Q. 17.

17. What was (PERSON) doing most of the past 12 months--

FOR FEMALES . . . keeping house, working or doing something else?

FOR MALES . . . working, or doing something else?

CIRCLE ONE CODE ONLY.

IF "SOMETHING ELSE," PROBE: What was (he/she) doing?

Working . . . . (SKIP TO Q. 19) 1

Keeping house . (SKIP TO Q. 19) 2

Going to school (SKIP TO Q. 21) 3

Retired . . . . (SKIP TO Q. 20) 4

Other . . (SPECIFY AND SKIP TO Q. 20) . 5

IF PERSON IS 14 THROUGH 16 YEARS OLD, ASK Q. 18.

18. What was (PERSON) doing most of the past 12 months--going to school or doing something else?

CIRCLE ONE CODE ONLY.

IF "SOMETHING ELSE," PROBE: What was (he/she) doing?

Going to school (SKIP TO Q. 21) 1

Working . . . . (GO TO Q. 19) 2

Keeping house . (GO TO Q. 19) 3

Other . . (SPECIFY AND SKIP TO Q. 22) . 4

IF "WORKING" OR "KEEPING HOUSE," ASK Q. 19.

19. In terms of health, is (PERSON) presently able to (work/keep house) at all?

Yes . . . . . . (ASK A) 1
No . . . . (SKIP TO Q. 23) 2

A. IF YES: Is (PERSON) limited in the kind of (work/housework) (he/she) can do, because of (his/her) health?

Yes . . . . (SKIP TO Q. 23) 3
No . . . . . . (ASK [1]) 4

[1] IF NO TO A: Is (PERSON) limited in the amount of (work/housework) (he/she) can do, because of (his/her) health?

Yes . . . . (SKIP TO Q. 23) 5
No . . . . . . (ASK [2]) 6

[2] IF NO TO [1]: Is (PERSON) limited in the kind of amount of other activities (he/she) can do, because of (his/her) health?

Yes . . . . (SKIP TO Q. 23) 7
No . . . . (SKIP TO Q. 24) 8

IF "RETIRED," OR "OTHER" IN Q. 17, ASK Q. 20.

20. Does (PERSON'S) health keep (him/her) from working?

Yes . . . . (SKIP TO Q. 23) 1
No . . . . . . (ASK A) 2

A. IF NO: Is (PERSON) limited in the kind of work (he/she) could do, because of (his/her) health?

Yes . . . . (SKIP TO Q. 23) 3
No . . . . . . (ASK [1]) 4

[1] IF NO TO A: Is (PERSON) limited in the amount of work (he/she) could do, because of (his/her) health?

Yes . . . . (SKIP TO Q. 23) 5
No . . . . . . (ASK [2]) 6

[2] IF NO TO [1]: Is (PERSON) limited in the kind or amount of other activities (he/she) can do, because of (his/her) activities?

Yes . . . . (SKIP TO Q. 23) 7
No . . . . (SKIP TO Q. 24) 8

IF "GOING TO SCHOOL," ASK Q. 21.

21. Does (PERSON) have to go to a certain type of school, because of (his/her) health?

Yes . . . . (SKIP TO Q. 23) 1

No . . . . . . (ASK A) 2

A. IF NO: Is (PERSON) limited in school attendance, because of (his/her) health?

Yes . . . . (SKIP TO Q. 23) 3

No . . . . . . (ASK [1]) 4

[1] IF NO TO A: Is (PERSON) limited in the kind or amount of other activities (he/she) can do, because of (his/her) health?

Yes . . . . (SKIP TO Q. 23) 5

No . . . . (SKIP TO Q. 24) 6

IF "OTHER" IN Q. 18, ASK Q. 22.

22. Does (PERSON'S) health keep (him/her) from going to school?

Yes . . . . (SKIP TO Q. 23) 1

No . . . . . . (ASK A) 2

A. IF NO: Would (PERSON) have to go to a certain type of school, because of (his/her) health?

Yes . . . . . (GO TO Q. 23) 3

No . . . . . . (ASK [1]) 4

[1] IF NO TO A: Would (PERSON) be limited in school attendance, because of (his/her) health?

Yes . . . . . (GO TO Q. 23) 5

No . . . . . . (ASK [2]) 6

[2] IF NO TO [1]: Is (PERSON) limited in the kind or amount of other activities (he/she) can do, because of (his/her) health?

Yes . . . . . (GO TO Q. 23) 7

No . . . . . (SKIP TO Q. 24) 8

23. ASK IF ANY LIMITATION BECAUSE OF HEALTH (FROM Q'S. 19, 20, 21, OR 22).

A. What condition causes this? RECORD BELOW NAME OF CONDITION OR SYMPTOMS, CAUSES, AND/OR PARTS OF BODY AFFECTED. (IF ANSWER IS "OLD AGE," RECORD VERBATIM AND PROBE: What specific condition causes this limitation?) PROBE, BEFORE GOING ON TO B: Is this limitation caused by any other conditions? (What are they?) PROBE AS ABOVE FOR NAME OR DESCRIPTION OF CONDITION. RECORD EACH CONDITION IN SEPARATE SPACE BELOW AND REPEAT PROBE.	B. ASK FOR EACH CONDITION IN A: Has (PERSON) had (CONDITION) for more than three months?	C. IF TWO OR MORE CONDITIONS IN A, ASK: Which of these conditions would you say is the main cause of (PERSON'S) limitation? CODE ONE CONDITION ONLY.
(1)	Yes . . . . 1 No 2	Main cause 1
(2)	Yes . . . . 1 No 2	Main cause 1
(3)	Yes . . . . 1 No 2	Main cause 1
(4)	Yes . . . . 1 No 2	Main cause 1
(5)	Yes . . . . 1 No 2	Main cause 1

ASK EVERYONE:

24. Thinking back over the last 12 months, that is, since (MONTH), 1967, was (PERSON)

kept from { going to work, going to school, doing (his/her) usual activity, } for at least two days in a row, because of an illness or accident?

Yes 1

No . . (SKIP TO INSTRUCTIONS BEFORE Q. 47, AT TOP OF PAGE 16.) . . 2

25. How many different times in the last 12 months was (PERSON) kept from (work/school/[his/her] usual activity) for at least 2 days in a row because of an illness or accident?

_________ times

26.

ASK Q. 26 FOR EACH TIME MENTIONED IN Q. 25, STARTING WITH THE MOST RECENT TIME. AFTER ASKING Q. 26 FOR ALL THE TIMES, THEN ASK Q. 26-A FOR EACH CONDITION.

(1) The last time this happened, what condition or health problems kept (PERSON) from (work/school/[his/her] usual activity)? RECORD NAME OF CONDITION, OR SYMPTOMS, CAUSES AND/OR PARTS OF BODY AFFECTED. IF MORE THAN ONE CONDITION AT SAME TIME, RECORD ALL IN SAME SPACE.

---

(2) The time before that, what condition or health problems kept (PERSON) from (work/school/[his/her] usual activity)?

---

(3) The time before that, what condition or health problems kept (PERSON) from (work/school/[his/her] usual activity)?

---

(4) The time before that, what condition or health problems kept (PERSON) from (work/school/[his/her] usual activity)?

---

(5) The time before that, what condition or health problems kept (PERSON) from (work/school/[his/her] usual activity)?

A.	B.
When did (PERSON) first (notice the CONDITION/ have the accident)--(aside from this particular attack of it)? RECORD BEGINNING DATE FOR EACH CONDITION. Month Year	IF NO DATES IN Q. 26-A ARE WITHIN LAST 12 MONTHS, SKIP TO INSTURCTIONS BEFORE Q. 47, AT TOP OF PAGE 16. IF ANY DATES ARE WITHIN LAST 12 MONTHS, CIRCLE "X" IN BOX ALONGSIDE MOST RECENT DATE. X
When did (PERSON) first (notice the CONDITION/ have the accident)--(aside from this particular attack of it)? Month Year	X
When did (PERSON) first (notice the CONDITION/ have the accident)--(aside from this particular attack of it)? Month Year	X
When did (PERSON) first (notice the CONDITION/ have the accident)--(aside from this particular attack of it)? Month Year	X
When did (PERSON) first (notice the CONDITION/ have the accident)--(aside from this particular attack of it)? Month Year	X

ASK FOR THE CONDITION CODED "X": Now, let's make sure I have this right--(PERSON) was kept from (ACTIVITY) for at least two days during the last 12 months because of (CONDITION X); is that correct?

IF CORRECT, GO ON TO Q. 27. IF INCORRECT, GO BACK AND CORRECT.

27. Now I'm going to ask you a few questions about (CONDITION "X" FROM Q. 26). When (PERSON) first (noticed CONDITION/had the accident), at the very beginning, how serious did (he/she) think it was--very serious, fairly serious, or not serious at all?

Very serious 1

Fairly serious 2

Not serious at all 3

---

28. When (PERSON) first (noticed CONDITION/had the accident) did (he/she) talk to anyone living in the household about <u>what to do about it</u>?

Yes . . . (ASK A & B) . . . 4

<u>IF YES, ASK A & B</u>: No 5

A. <u>IF OBVIOUS, CODE WITHOUT ASKING</u>. Who did (PERSON) talk to? CODE AS MANY AS APPLY.	B. ASK FOR EACH. What did (PERSON NAMED IN "A") think (he/she) should do?
Spouse 1	___
Other person 2	___
Other person 3	___

---

29. When (PERSON) first (noticed CONDITION/had the accident), did (he/she), or anyone in the household, talk with someone who <u>doesn't</u> live here about <u>what to do about it</u>--a relative; friend or neighbor; a nurse; a druggist; or someone else, not counting a doctor?

Yes . . . (ASK A & B) . . . 1

<u>IF YES, ASK A & B</u>: No 2

A. Who was that? CODE AS MANY AS APPLY. READ CATEGORIES, IF NECESSARY.	B. ASK FOR EACH. What did (PERSON NAMED IN "A") think (he/she) should do?
Relative, friend, or neighbor 3	___
Nurse 4	___
Druggist 5	___
Other person 6	___
Other person 7	___

30. Did (PERSON), or anyone on the household, see or talk to a doctor about (PERSON'S) (CONDITION/accident)?

Yes 1

No . . (SKIP TO Q. 42) . 2

---

31. Was the doctor that was seen or talked to the first time, the doctor (PERSON) usually goes to?

Yes 3

No 4

---

32. How soon was it after (PERSON) first (noticed CONDITION/had the accident) that the doctor was seen, or talked to on the phone? About how many days?

(RECORD NUMBER OF DAYS OR CODE "SAME DAY.") _________ days

Same day as first (noticed condition/had accident) . . 00

---

33. Please look at this card and tell me where that first call or visit was.

HAND CARD A

First saw a doctor at:

Hospital emergency room 1

Hospital clinic 2

Clinic not connected with a hospital (including a union or H.I.P. clinic) 3

Private doctor, in his office 4

Private doctor, in your home 5

First talked on the phone, to a:

Private doctor 6

Union or H.I.P. doctor 7

First saw or talked to a doctor somewhere else (SPECIFY) 8

IF INFORMATION VOLUNTEERED THAT PERSON WAS KEPT, OR SENT, TO STAY OVERNIGHT IN HOSPITAL AT FIRST CALL OR VISIT, CIRCLE CODE X BELOW.

Went directly to hospital . . . (SKIP TO Q. 41) X

---

34. Did the doctor prescribe, or give (PERSON) any medicine or shots that first time?

Yes 6

No 7

IF FIRST CONTACT WITH DOCTOR WAS A PHONE CALL, SKIP TO Q. 36.

35. Did (PERSON) have any tests or X-rays during that first visit?

Yes 8

No 9

36. When (PERSON) talked to the doctor that first time for (CONDITION), did he tell (him/her) to (come back/come in)?

Yes . . . (ASK A) 1
No 2

A. IF YES: Did (he/she)?

Yes 3
No . . . (ASK [1]) . . . 4

[1] IF NO TO A: Why didn't (he/she)?

Not time yet 5
Other . . (SPECIFY) . . . 6

---

37. How many times altogether, including that first time, was any doctor seen or talked to about this (condition/accident)?

_________ times

First time only . (SKIP TO Q. 40) . . 01

---

38. Was it the same (doctor/place) every time?

Yes 1
No . . . (ASK A) 2

A. IF NO: How did (PERSON) decide to go to a different (doctor/place)--did the first (doctor/place) send (him/her) to the second one, or did (he/she) or the family decide to see another doctor, or what?

Sent by first doctor . . . 3
Own or family decision . . 4
Other . . (SPECIFY) 5

---

39. Did (PERSON) have any (other) tests or X-rays during any visit after the first time for this (condition/accident)?

Yes 6
No 7

---

40. Did any doctor (PERSON) saw or talked to suggest that (he/she) should stay overnight in a hospital for (CONDITION)?

Yes . . . (ASK A) 1
No 2

A. IF YES: Did (he/she)?

Yes 3
No . . . (ASK [1]) . . . 4

[1] IF NO TO A: Why didn't (he/she)?

41. Does (PERSON) expect to see or talk to a doctor again about this particular condition?

Yes 5

No 6

Depends 7

---

42. Did (PERSON) take any kind of medicine for (CONDITION)?

Yes . . . (ASK A) 1

No 2

A. IF YES: Was (any of) this medicine prescribed by a doctor?

Yes 3

No . . . (ASK [1]) . . . 4

[1] IF NO TO A: Was (any of) this medicine bought in a drugstore?

Yes 5

No 6

---

43. Thinking about this time when (PERSON) had (CONDITION), how many days altogether was it that (he/she) couldn't (go to work) (go to school) (do [his/her] usual activity)? PROBE FOR BEST GUESS.

__________ days

---

44. About how many of those days did (PERSON) have to stay in bed, all or most of the day, because of this (condition/accident)? PROBE FOR BEST GUESS.

__________ days

---

45. Was this the first time (PERSON) has had (CONDITION)?

Yes 1

No 2

---

46. Is (PERSON) limited in any way in what (he/she) can do now, because of this (condition/accident)?

Yes 3

No 4

IF PERSON IS MALE, SKIP TO Q. 50.
IF PERSON IS FEMALE OVER 50 YEARS, SKIP TO Q. 50.

And now a few questions about pregnancy.

47. Is (PERSON) pregnant now?

Yes 1

No 2

---

48. (Besides this pregnancy . . .) Has (PERSON) been pregnant in the last 12 months--that is, since (MONTH), 1967? I'm interested in any pregnancy, even if it ended in a miscarriage.

Yes . . . . . (ASK A-E) 3

No . . . (SKIP TO Q. 50) . . . 4

IF YES:

A. How did the pregnancy end--was it a live birth, a miscarriage, or what?

Live birth 5

Miscarriage 6

Stillbirth 7

B. How many months along was she when the pregnancy ended?

Less than 3 months 1

3, 4, or 5 months 2

6 months 3

7 months 4

8 months 5

9 months 6

10 months 7

D. Did she see a doctor about her pregnancy at any time before (the baby was born/the miscarriage)?

Yes . . . (ASK [1]&[2]) 1

No . . . . . (GO TO D) 2

IF YES TO C:

[1] How many times?

_________ visits

[2] How many months pregnant was she when she first saw a doctor?

_________ months

D. Did she have a check-up for this pregnancy a month or two after (the baby was born/the miscarriage)?

Yes 1

No 2

E. IF MISCARRIAGE, DO NOT ASK E:

Was the baby delivered by a doctor?

Yes 3

No 4

Q. 49 OMITTED.

ASK EVERYONE:

50. (IF HOSPITALIZATION IN LAST 12 MONTHS ALREADY MENTIONED, CODE "YES" TO Q. 50 WITHOUT ASKING, AND GO ON TO Q. 50-A.)

Has (PERSON) been a patient in a hospital at any time in the last 12 months--since (MONTH), 1967?

Yes . . . (ASK A) 1

No 2

A. IF YES: Altogether, how many different times was (PERSON) a hospital patient, since (MONTH), 1967?

_________ times

---

51. Has (PERSON) been a patient in a nursing home, convalescent home, or any place like that, in the last 12 months--since (MONTH), 1967?

Yes . . . . (ASK A) 1

No . (SKIP TO INSTRUCTION AT BOTTOM OF THIS PAGE) 2

A. IF YES: Altogether, how many different times was (PERSON) a patient in a nursing home, or any place like that, since (MONTH), 1967?

_______ times

IF PERSON WAS IN A HOSPITAL, NURSING HOME, OR SIMILAR PLACE IN LAST 12 MONTHS (YES TO Q'S. 50 OR 51), ASK Q. 52, ON NEXT PAGE.

IF NO TO BOTH Q'S. 50 AND 51, SKIP TO Q. 53, ON PAGE 20.

52. ASK A-F ABOUT EACH DIFFERENT STAY IN A HOSPITAL OR NURSING HOME (OR SIMILAR PLACE) IN THE LAST 12 MONTHS. START WITH THE MOST RECENT STAY. ASK A-F FOR EACH STAY BEFORE GOING ON TO THE STAY BEFORE THAT.

I'm going to ask a few questions about the time(s) (PERSON) was in the hospital (nursing home). (Let's start with the last time.)

	Most recent stay	Stay before that
A. When did (he/she) enter the (hospital/nursing home) (that time)? PROBE FOR MONTH AND YEAR.	______ Month Year	______ Month Year
B. How many nights was (he/she) in the (hospital/nursing home) (that time)?	______ Nights	______ Nights
C. What is the name and address of this (hospital/nursing home)? RECORD NAME, ADDRESS OR DESCRIPTION, AND CITY.	Name: ______ Add.: ______ City: ______	Name: ______ Add.: ______ City: ______
D. For what condition did (he/she) enter the (hospital/nursing home)--do you know the medical name? IF NAME NOT KNOWN, PROBE FOR SYMPTOMS, CAUSES, AND/OR PARTS OF BODY AFFECTED.		
E. Did (he/she) have any operations during this stay at the (hospital/nursing home)?	Yes (ASK [1]&[2]) . 1 No 2	Yes (ASK [1]&[2]) . 1 No 1
IF YES TO E: [1] Can you tell me the name, or what kind of operation that was? IF NAME NOT KNOWN, PROBE FOR DESCRIPTION OF WHAT WAS DONE.		
[2] Any other operation (that time)? (IF YES: DESCRIBE.)	One operation only 1 Yes, other operation 2	One operation only 1 Yes, other operation . . . 2

IF HOSPITALIZATION WAS FOR CHILDBIRTH, DO NOT ASK F.

F. Did (PERSON) see a doctor about (CONDITION) after (he/she) got out of the hospital?	Yes . . . . 3 No 4	Yes . . . . 3 No 4

Stay before that	Stay before that	Stay before that
Month Year	Month Year	Month Year
Nights	Nights	Nights
Name: Add.: City:	Name: Add.: City:	Name: Add.: City:
Yes . (ASK [1]&[2]) . . 1 No 2	Yes . (ASK [1]&[2]) . 1 No 2	Yes . (ASK [1]&[2]) . 1 No 2
One operation only . . 1 Yes, other operation 2	One operation only . 1 Yes, other operation 2	One operation only . 1 Yes, other operation 2
Yes . . . . 3 No 4	Yes . . . . 3 No 4	Yes . . . . 3 No 4

ASK EVERYONE:

53. When was the last time (PERSON) had a general physical check-up? (Just your best guess.)

____
(MONTH) (YEAR)

Never had one 0

Q. 54 OMITTED

55. About how long has it been since (PERSON) saw or talked to a medical doctor about (his/her) own health--for any kind of condition, even for a few minutes?

________ months OR ________ years

IF MORE THAN 12 MONTHS, SKIP TO Q. 57.

56. Altogether (including the visits we have already talked about), how many times in the last 12 months did (PERSON) see or talk to a doctor, or go to any of these places, about (his/her) own health? First, to a hospital emergency room? . . . READ EACH CODE CATEGORY, AND RECORD NUMBER OF VISITS TO EACH. RECORD "0" IF NONE.

	# OF CONTACTS
A. Hospital emergency room	
B. Hospital out-patient clinic	
C. Clinic not connected with a hospital	
D. Private doctor, in his office	
E. Talk to a private doctor, over the telephone	
F. See a private doctor, in your home	
G. Did (PERSON) go anywhere else to see a doctor (not counting visits by a doctor while [he/she] was a patient in a hospital)? (IF YES, SPECIFY.)	
Total Contacts:	

That's a total of ________ visits and calls in the last 12 months--does that sound right? (IF NOT RIGHT, GO OVER CATEGORIES WITH RESPONDENT.)

57. Altogether during the last 12 months, how many days did (PERSON) have to stay in bed, all or most of the day, because of illness or injury?

________ days

IF PERSON IS 65 OR OVER, ASK Q. 58.

58. Does (PERSON) have a Medicare card?

Yes . . . (ASK A) 1
No 2

A. IF YES: It would be helpful if I could see (his/her) Medicare card to find out about the coverage--may I see it?

CODE TYPE(S) OF COVERAGE FROM CARD, OR CIRCLE APPROPRIATE "NO CARD SHOWN" CODE.

From Card:

Hospital coverage 3
Doctor (Medical) coverage 4
No coverage shown . (ASK [1]) 5

"No Card Shown":

Can't locate card . (ASK [1]) 6
Refused . . . . . . (ASK [1]) 7

[1] IF NO COVERAGE SHOWN, OR "NO CARD SHOWN" (CODES 5, 6, OR 7 CIRCLED IN A):

If (he/she) covered by that part of Medicare that pays for doctor's bills--that is, the Medicare plan for which (PERSON)--(or some agency)--must pay $4.00 a month?

Yes 4
No 5
Don't know 6

IF PERSON IS MALE, 17 YEARS OR OVER, ASK Q. 59.

59. I'm going to read a list of reasons people sometimes give for not seeing a medical doctor when perhaps they should. Please tell me, for each of these reasons, whether or not it has ever kept (PERSON) from seeing a doctor . . . (as far as you know . . .) READ ITEMS, AND CIRCLE ONE CODE FOR EACH.

	Yes	No	Don't Know	Doesn't Apply; Never Worked
A. (PERSON) didn't want to lose time or pay from work? (Did that ever keep him from seeing a doctor when perhaps he should have?)	1	2	3	4
B. He was worried that his boss might think he was too sick to work?	5	6	7	8
C. He didn't think a doctor could help him? (Did that ever keep him from seeing a doctor when perhaps he should have?) . . .	1	2	3	-
D. The doctor or place didn't have office hours that were convenient for him? . . .	4	5	6	-

ASK EVERYONE:

60. About how long has it been since (PERSON) was last treated or examined by a dentist?

_______ months or _______ years

Never X

IF WITHIN LAST 12 MONTHS, ASK A-D:

A. How many times has (PERSON) been to a dentist in the last 12 months?

_______ visits

B. When (he/she) last saw a dentist, was it for an emergency visit?

Yes 7

No 8

C. What has (he/she) had done by a dentist or assistant during the last 12 months? First, has (he/she) had (his/her) teeth checked, X-rayed or cleaned?

READ EACH ITEM, AND CODE "YES" OR "NO" FOR EACH.

	Yes	No
(1) Teeth checked, X-rayed, or cleaned	1	2
(2) Teeth fixed or filled	3	4
(3) Bridgework repaired	5	6
(4) Teeth or bridgework replaced	7	8
(5) Tooth or teeth pulled	1	2
(6) Any other work? (SPECIFY)	3	4

D. How long does it usually take (PERSON) to get to the dentist? (The way [he/she] usually goes.)

0-9 minutes 1

10-19 minutes 2

20-29 minutes 3

30-39 minutes 4

40-49 minutes 5

50-59 minutes 6

1 hour or more 7

Sees school dentist . . . 8

Now just a few background questions.

61. What is the highest grade or year (PERSON) completed in school?

No schooling	01
1st to 2nd grade	02
3rd to 4th grade	03
5th to 7th grade	04
8th grade	05
9th grade	06
High school, incomplete (grades 10 or 11)	07
High school, incomplete--plus voactional or business school	08
High school, complete (12th grade)	09
Vocational or business school, in addition to completing high school	10
College, incomplete	11
College, complete	12
Don't know	13

---

62. IF OBVIOUS, CODE WITHOUT ASKING. Is (PERSON) currently married, widowed, divorced, separated, or never married?

Married	1
Widowed	2
Divorced	3
Separated	4
Never married	5

IF PERSON WAS "KEEPING HOUSE" OR "GOING TO SCHOOL" FOR MOST OF LAST 12 MONTHS (FROM Q'S. 17 OR 18), DO NOT ASK Q. 63--SKIP TO INSTRUCTIONS IN BOX BELOW.

ALL OTHERS, ASK Q. 63.

63. A. What kind of work does (PERSON) (did [PERSON] normally) do?

(PROBE, IF VAGUE: What [does/did] [he/she] actually do on that job?)

B. What kind of business or industry is that?

(PROBE, IF VAGUE: What does that [firm/organization/agency] make or do?)

IF PERSON IS 17 OR OVER, AND NOT RELATED TO HEAD OF HOUSEHOLD OR HEAD'S WIFE, GO ON TO ASK Q'S. 68-83 ON NEXT PAGES.

OTHERWISE, THIS IS THE END OF THE BLUE BOOKLET FOR THIS PERSON: FILL OUT ITEMS ON BACK OF BOOKLET AFTER LEAVING HOUSEHOLD.

ASK QUESTIONS ON PAGES 25-27 ONLY IF YOU ARE INTERVIEWING A PERSON 17 OR OVER WHO IS UNRELATED TO HEAD OR WIFE OF HEAD.

68. Have you been enrolled in Medicaid any time in the last 12 months? (Medicaid is a Medial Assistance Program, which is handled through the New York City Department of Social Services.)

Yes . . . . (ASK A & B) 1

No 2

IF YES:

A. Are you covered by Medicaid now?

Yes 3

No 4

B. Have you used Medicaid in the last 12 months?

Yes 5

No 6

---

72. (Not counting Medicare or Medicaid) . . . Have you any insurance that pays all or part of the medical bills when you go to the hospital or doctor--such as Blue Cross/Blue Shield, a commercial plan, a union plan, or some other plan?

Yes . . . . (ASK A - C) 1

No 2

IF YES:

A. Does this insurance pay for just hospital bills, just doctor bills, or both hospital and doctor bills?

Hospital only 1

Doctor only 2

Both 3

B. What is the name of the insurance plan? (Any others?)

C. (Was this insurance plan/Were these insurance plans) gotten through an employer, a union, directly from a salesman, or what?

Employer 1

Union 2

Salesman 3

Other (SPECIFY) 4

82. We would like to get an idea of how much money people get from different places.

A. How much do you earn, each week, from any jobs--wages or salary--before taxes? (ENTER TOTAL WEEKLY WAGES, OR CIRCLE "0"; THEN ASK [1].)

$________ Weekly

None 0

[1] Would you say this figure is higher, about the same, or lower than your usual weekly income over the last 12 months?

Higher 1

About same . . 2

Lower 3

B. Do you get any income from Welfare? (IF YES: How much money does that come to altogether, each month?) (ENTER TOTAL MONTHLY AMOUNT, OR CIRCLE "0")

$________ Monthly

None 0

C. How much money, if any, do you get, each month, from the following sources:

[1] Social Security or other retirement payments or pensions? (ENTER TOTAL MONTHLY AMOUNT, OR CIRCLE "0")

$________ Monthly

None 0

[2] V.A. payments or Armed Forces allotments? (ENTER TOTAL MONTHLY AMOUNT, OR CIRCLE "0")

$________ Monthly

None 0

[3] Interest, or rental payments? (ENTER TOTAL MONTHLY AMOUNT, OR CIRCLE "0")

$________ Monthly

None 0

[4] Any other sources, such as (child support payments), gifts, or anything else? (ENTER TOTAL MONTHLY AMOUNT, OR CIRCLE "0")

$________ Monthly

None 0

83. Which of these groups on this card includes your total income during last year--1967? That is, all income, from any sources, before taxes. Just tell me the letter for the amount that fits.

HAND CARD B

A.	$ 0 - $ 499	00
B.	500 - 999	01
C.	1,000 - 1,499	02
D.	1,500 - 1,999	03
E.	2,000 - 2,499	04
F.	2,500 - 2,999	05
G.	3,000 - 3,499	06
H.	3,500 - 3,999	07
I.	4,000 - 4,499	08
J.	4,500 - 4,999	09
K.	5,000 - 5,999	10
L.	6,000 - 6,999	11
M.	7,000 - 7,999	12
N.	8,000 - 8,999	13
O.	9,000 - 9,999	14
P.	10,000 and over	15
	Don't know	99
	Refused	xx

END OF BLUE BOOKLET.
FILL OUT ITEMS ON BACK PAGE IMMEDIATELY
AFTER LEAVING HOUSEHOLD.

FILL OUT ITEMS BELOW IMMEDIATELY AFTER LEAVING HOUSEHOLD

A. Date of interview: ______________________________

B. Interviewer's signature: ____

C. Respondent for this questionnaire was:

Respondent on main questionnaire . . 00

Someone else . . (ANSWER [1]) . . . R

[1] IF SOMEONE ELSE: Who?

NAME: ____

PERSON NO.: . . . . [|]

CONFIDENTIAL
4055
9/68

Approved through-June 30, 1968

Form approved.
Budget Bureau No. 116-R0146

NATIONAL OPINION RESEARCH CENTER
University of Chicago

OFFICE OF ECONOMIC OPPORTUNITY

NEIGHBORHOOD HEALTH CENTER SURVEY

"PINK BOOKLET"--FOR CHILDREN
IN HOUSEHOLD UNDER 14

SEGMENT # ______________ PERSON'S NAME: ______________________________

DULS LINE # ____________ PERSON'S #: ______________________________

Now, we need the same kind of information about (CHILD).

5. In general, would you say (CHILD'S) health is excellent, good, fair, or poor?

Excellent 1

Good 2

Fair 3

Poor 4

Don't know 5

6. Who does (CHILD) see, or where do you take (him/her), most of the time when you want to see a doctor for (him/her)--to what doctor or place?

NAME OF DOCTOR OR PLACE: ______________________________

ADDRESS OR DESCRIPTION: ______________________________

____

CODE LOCATION: In community 6

Out of community . . . 7

SAME DOCTOR OR PLACE AS NAMED FOR ANY OTHER HOUSEHOLD MEMBER . . . . (SKIP TO Q. 12) X

Never goes anywhere (SKIP TO Q. 12) . . 8

---

7. IF OBVIOUS, CODE WITHOUT ASKING: Is that a private doctor, a hospital clinic or emergency room, a chiropractor, a union or H.I.P. doctor or what?

Private doctor . . . . (ASK A) 1

Hospital clinic or emergency room . . . 2

Chiropractor 3

Union or H.I.P. doctor . . (ASK A) . . 4

Other (SPECIFY) 5

A. IF PRIVATE, UNION, OR H.I.P. DOCTOR: Is he a general practitioner or some kind of specialist?

General practitioner 7

Specialist . . . . . (ASK [1]) 8

Don't know 9

[1] IF SPECIALIST: What kind of specialist is he?

8. When did (CHILD) first start going to (DOCTOR OR PLACE NAMED IN Q. 6)--within the last 12 months or longer ago than that?

Within last 12 months 1

Longer ago than that 2

---

9. OMITTED

---

10. How long does it usually take (you/CHILD) to get there (the way [you/CHILD] usually go[es])?

0-9 minutes 1

10-19 minutes 2

20-29 minutes 3

30-39 minutes 4

40-49 minutes 5

50-59 minutes 6

1 hour or more 7

Never went from this address 8

Never went . . . (SKIP TO Q. 12) . . . 9

---

11. Once (CHILD) gets there, about how long does (he/she) usually have to wait to see the doctor?

Less than 1/2 hour 1

1/2 to less than one hour 2

One to less than 1-1/2 hours 3

More than 1-1/2 hours 4

12. Of all the doctors and places you know of, when something worries you about (CHILD'S) health, is there any one doctor or place that you trust more than any other, to get medical help or advice? (DO NOT PROBE.)

Yes . . . . (ASK A) 1

No . . . . . (SKIP TO Q. 18) 2

A. IF YES: What doctor or place?

NAME OF DOCTOR OR PLACE: ______________________

ADDRESS OR DESCRIPTION: ______________________

____

CODE LOCATION: In community 6

Out of community . . . 7

SAME DOCTOR OR PLACE AS NAMED IN Q. 6, OR FOR ANY OTHER HOUSEHOLD MEMBER . . . . (SKIP TO Q. 18) X

---

13. IF OBVIOUS, CODE WITHOUT ASKING: Is that a private doctor, a hospital clinic or emergency room, a chiropractor, a union or H.I.P. doctor, or what?

Private doctor . . . . (ASK A) 1

Hospital clinic or emergency room . . . 2

Chiropractor 3

Union or H.I.P. doctor . . (ASK A) . . 4

Other . . . . . . (SPECIFY) 5

A. IF PRIVATE, UNION, OR H.I.P. DOCTOR: Is he a general practitioner or some kind of specialist?

General practitioner 7

Specialist . . . . . (ASK [1]) 8

Don't know 9

[1] IF SPECIALIST: What kind of specialist is he?

14. When you get medical help or advice for (CHILD), how often do you get it from (DOCTOR OR PLACE NAMED IN Q. 12)--some of the time, hardly ever, or never?

Some of the time 1

Hardly ever 2

Never . . . . . (SKIP TO Q. 18) 3

---

15. How long does it usually take (you/CHILD) to get there (the way [you/ CHILD] usually go[es])?

0-9 minutes 1

10-19 minutes 2

20-29 minutes 3

30-39 minutes 4

40-49 minutes 5

50-59 minutes 6

1 hour or more 7

---

16. Once (CHILD) gets there, about how long does (he/she) usually have to wait to see the doctor?

Less than 1/2 hour 1

1/2 to less than one hour 2

One hour to less than 1-1/2 hours 3

More than 1-1/2 hours 4

Don't know 5

Q. 17 OMITTED.

IF CHILD IS 6 THROUGH 13 YEARS OLD, ASK Q. 18.

18. What was (CHILD) doing most of the past 12 months--going to school or something else?

CIRCLE ONE CODE ONLY. IF "SOMETHING ELSE," PROBE: What was (CHILD) doing?

Going to school (SKIP TO Q. 21) 1

Other . . (SPECIFY AND SKIP TO Q. 22) . 4

IF CHILD IS 1 THROUGH 5 YEARS OLD, ASK Q. C-19.

C-19. Is (CHILD) able to take part at all in ordinary play with other children?

Yes . . . . . . (ASK A) 3

No . . . . (SKIP TO Q. 23) 4

A. IF YES: Is (he/she) limited in the kind of play (he/she) can do, because of (his/her) health?

Yes . . . . (SKIP TO Q. 23) 5

No . . . . (ASK [1]) 6

[1] IF NO TO A: Is (he/she) limited in the amount of play, because of (his/her) health?

Yes . . . . (SKIP TO Q. 23) 7

No . . . . (SKIP TO Q. 24) 8

IF CHILD IS UNDER 1 YEAR, ASK Q. C-20.

C-20. Is (CHILD) limited in any way because of (his/her) health?

Yes . . . . . . (ASK A) 1

No . . . . (SKIP TO Q. 24) 2

A. IF YES: In what way is (he/she) limited? (SPECIFY, AND THEN SKIP TO Q. 23.)

IF "GOING TO SCHOOL," ASK Q. 21.

21. Does (CHILD) have to go to a certain type of school, because of (his/her) health?

Yes . . . . (SKIP TO Q. 23) 1

No . . . . . . (ASK A) 2

A. IF NO: Is (he/she) limited in school attendance, because of (his/her) health?

Yes . . . . (SKIP TO Q. 23) 3

No . . . . . . (ASK [1]) 4

[1] IF NO TO A: Is (he/she) limited in the kind or amount of other activities (he/she) can do, because of (his/her) health?

Yes . . . . (SKIP TO Q. 23) 5

No . . . . (SKIP TO Q. 24) 6

IF "OTHER" IN Q. 18, ASK Q. 22.

22. Does (CHILD'S) health keep (him/her) from going to school?

Yes . . . . (SKIP TO Q. 23) 1

No . . . . . . (ASK A) 2

A. IF NO: Would (he/she) have to go to a certain type of school, because of (his/her) health?

Yes . . . . . (GO TO Q. 23) 3

No . . . . . . (ASK [1]) 4

[1] IF NO TO A: Would (he/she) be limited in school attendance, because of (his/her) health?

Yes . . . . . (GO TO Q. 23) 5

No . . . . . . (ASK [2]) 6

[2] IF NO TO [1]: Is (he/she) limited in the kind or amount of other activities (he/she) can do, because of (his/her) health?

Yes . . . . . (GO TO Q. 23) 7

No . . . . (SKIP TO Q. 24) 8

23. ASK IF ANY LIMITATION BECAUSE OF HEALTH (FROM Q'S. C-19, C-20, 21, or 22).

A. What condition causes this? RECORD BELOW NAME OF CONDITION OR SYMPTOMS, CAUSES, AND/OR PARTS OF BODY AFFECTED. PROBE, BEFORE GOING ON TO B: Is this limitation caused by any other conditions? (What are they?) PROBE AS ABOVE FOR NAME OR DESCRIPTION OF CONDITION. RECORD EACH CONDITION IN SEPARATE SPACE BELOW AND REPEAT PROBE.	B. ASK FOR EACH CONDITION IN A: Has (CHILD) had (CONDITION) for more than three months?	C. IF TWO OR MORE CONDITIONS IN A, ASK: Which of these conditions would you say is the main cause of (CHILD'S) limitation? CODE ONE CONDITION ONLY.
(1)	Yes . . . . 1 No 2	Main cause 1
(2)	Yes . . . . 1 No 2	Main cause 1
(3)	Yes . . . . 1 No 2	Main cause 1
(4)	Yes . . . . 1 No 2	Main cause 1
(5)	Yes . . . . 1 No 2	Main cause 1

ASK EVERYONE:

24. Thinking back over the last 12 months, that is, since (MONTH), 1967 . . .

{ was (CHILD) kept from going to school, / did (CHILD) not act like (he/she) usually does, } for at least two days in a row, because of an illness or accident?

Yes 1

No . . (SKIP TO Q. 50, ON PAGE 17) . . 2

25. How many different times in the last 12 months was it that (CHILD) (couldn't go to school) (did not act like [he/she] usually does)--for at at least 2 days in a row, because of an illness or accident?

_________ times

26.

ASK Q. 26 FOR EACH TIME MENTIONED IN Q. 25, STARTING WITH THE MOST RECENT TIME. AFTER ASKING Q. 26 FOR ALL THE TIMES, THEN ASK Q. 26-A FOR EACH CONDITION.

(1) The last time this happened, what condition or health problems kept (CHILD) from (going to school) (acting like [he/she] usually does)? RECORD NAME OF CONDITION, OR SYMPTOMS, CAUSES AND/OR PARTS OF BODY AFFECTED. IF MORE THAN ONE CONDITION, AT SAME TIME, RECORD ALL IN SAME SPACE.

---

(2) The time before that, what condition or health problems kept (CHILD) from (going to school) (acting like [he/she] usually does)?

---

(3) The time before that, what condition or health problems kept (CHILD) from (going to school) (acting like [he/she] usually does)?

---

(4) The time before that, what condition or health problems kept (CHILD) from (going to school) (acting like [he/she] usually does)?

---

(5) The time before that, what condition or health problems kept (CHILD) from (going to school) (acting like [he/she] usually does)?

A. When did (you first notice the CONDITION/the accident happen)--(aside from this particular attack of it)? RECORD BEGINNING DATE FOR EACH CONDITION. Month Year	IF NO DATES IN Q. 26-A ARE WITHIN LAST 12 MONTHS, SKIP TO Q. 50, ON PAGE 17. IF ANY DATES ARE WITHIN LAST 12 MONTHS, CIRCLE "X" IN BOX ALONGSIDE MOST RECENT DATE. X
When did (you first notice the CONDITION/the accident happen)--(aside from this particular attack of it)? Month Year	X
When did (you first notice the CONDITION/the accident happen)--(aside from this particular attack of it)? Month Year	X
When did (you first notice the CONDITION/the accident happen)--(aside from this particular attack of it)? Month Year	X
When did (you first notice the CONDITION/the accident happen)--(aside from this particular attack of it)? Month Year	X

ASK FOR THE CONDITION CODED "X": Now, let's make sure I have this right--(CHILD) was kept from (ACTIVITY) for at least two days during the last 12 months because of (CONDITION X); is that correct?

IF CORRECT, GO ON TO Q. 27. IF INCORRECT, GO BACK AND CORRECT.

27. Now I'm going to ask you a few questions about (CONDITION "X" FROM Q. 26). When (you first noticed CONDITION/the accident happened), at the very beginning, how serious did you think it was--very serious, fairly serious, or not serious at all?

Very serious 1
Fairly serious 2
Not serious at all . . . 3

---

28. When (you first noticed CONDITION/the accident happened), did you (CHILD'S mother) talk to anyone living in the household about what to do about it?

Yes . . (ASK A & B) . . . 4
No 5

IF YES, ASK A & B:

A. IF OBVIOUS, CODE WITHOUT ASKING: Who did you (CHILD'S mother) talk to? CODE AS MANY AS APPLY.	B. ASK FOR EACH. What did (PERSON NAMED IN A) think you should do?
Spouse (of respondent or of child's mother) 1	______
Other person 2	______
Other person 3	______

---

29. When (you first noticed CONDITION/the accident happened), did you, or anyone in the household, talk with someone who doesn't live here about what to do about it--a relative; friend or neighbor; a nurse; a druggist; or somone else, other than a doctor?

Yes . . (ASK A & B) . . . 1
No 2

IF YES, ASK A & B:

A. Who was that? CODE AS MANY AS APPLY. READ CATEGORIES, IF NECESSARY.	B. ASK FOR EACH. What did (PERSON NAMED IN A) think you should do?
Relative, friend, or neighbor 3	______
Nurse 4	______
Druggist 5	______
Other person 6	______
Other person 7	______

30. Did a doctor see (CHILD), or did you, or anyone in the household, see or talk to a doctor about (CHILD'S) (CONDITION/accident)?

Yes 1

No . . (SKIP TO Q. 42) . 2

---

31. Was the doctor that was seen or talked to the first time the doctor (CHILD) usually goes to?

Yes 3

No 4

---

32. How soon was it after (you first noticed CONDITION/the accident happened) that the doctor was seen, or talked to on the phone? About how many days?

(RECORD NUMBER OF DAYS OR CODE "SAME DAY.") __________ days

Same day as first (noticed condition/had accident) . . 00

---

33. Please look at this card and tell me where that first call or visit was.

HAND CARD A

First saw a doctor at:

Hospital emergency room 1

Hospital clinic 2

Clinic not connected with a hospital (including a union or H.I.P. clinic) 3

Private doctor, in his office 4

Private doctor, in your home 5

First talked on the phone, to a:

Private doctor 6

Union or H.I.P. doctor 7

First saw or talked to a doctor somewhere else (SPECIFY) 8

IF INFORMATION VOLUNTEERED THAT CHILD WAS KEPT, OR SENT, TO STAY OVERNIGHT IN HOSPITAL AT FIRST CALL OR VISIT, CIRCLE CODE X BELOW.

Went directly to hospital . . . (SKIP TO Q. 41) X

---

34. Did the doctor prescribe, or give (CHILD) any medicine or shots that first time?

Yes 6

No 7

IF FIRST CONTACT WITH DOCTOR WAS A PHONE CALL, SKIP TO Q. 36.

35. Did (CHILD) have any tests or X-rays during that first visit?

Yes 8

No 9

36. When the doctor was talked to that first time for (CONDITION), did he tell (you/CHILD) to (come back/come in)?

Yes . . . (ASK A) 1
No 2

A. IF YES: Did (you/he/she)?

Yes 3
No . . . (ASK [1]) . . . 4

[1] IF NO TO A: Why didn't (you/he/she)?

Not time yet 5
Other . . (SPECIFY) . . . 6

---

37. How many times altogether, including that first time, was any doctor seen or talked to about this (condition/accident)?

__________ times

First time only . (SKIP TO Q. 40) . . 01

---

38. Was it the same doctor every time?

Yes 1
No . . . (ASK A) 2

A. IF NO: How did you decide to go to a different doctor--did the first doctor send you to the second one, or did you or your family decide to see another doctor, or what?

Sent by first doctor . . 3
Own or family decision . 4
Other . . (SPECIFY) . . . 5

---

39. Did (CHILD) have any (other) tests or X-rays during any visit after the first time for this (condition/accident)?

Yes 6
No 7

---

40. Did any doctor who saw (CHILD), or who you or anyone in the household saw or talked to, suggest that (CHILD) should stay overnight in a hospital for (CONDITION)?

Yes . . . (ASK A) 1
No 2

A. IF YES: Did (he/she)?

Yes 3
No . . . (ASK [1]) . . . 4

[1] IF NO TO A: Why didn't (he/she)?

41. Do you expect that a doctor will see (CHILD) again about this particular condition?

Yes 5

No 6

Depends 7

---

42. Did (CHILD) take any kind of medicine for (CONDITION)?

Yes . . . (ASK A) 1

No 2

A. IF YES: Was (any of) this medicine prescribed by a doctor?

Yes 3

No . . . (ASK [1]) . . . 4

[1] IF NO TO A: Was (any of) this medicine bought in a drugstore?

Yes 5

No 6

---

43. Thinking about this time when (CHILD) had (CONDITION), how many days altogether was it that (he/she) (couldn't go to school) (didn't act like [he/she] usually does)? PROBE FOR BEST GUESS.

__________ days

---

44. About how many of those days did (CHILD) have to stay in bed, all or most of the day, because of this (condition/accident)? PROBE FOR BEST GUESS.

__________ days

---

45. Was this the first time (CHILD) has had (CONDITION)?

Yes 1

No 2

---

46. Is (CHILD) limited in any way in what (he/she) can do now, because of this (condition/accident)?

Yes 3

No 4

Q'S. 47-49 OMITTED.

ASK EVERYONE:

50. (IF HOSPITALIZATION IN LAST 12 MONTHS ALREADY MENTIONED, CODE "YES" TO Q. 50 WITHOUT ASKING, AND GO ON TO 50-A.)

Has (CHILD) been a patient in a hospital at any time in the last 12 months--since (MONTH), 1967?

Yes . . . (ASK A) 1

No 2

A. IF YES: Altogether, how many different times was (he/she) a hospital patient, since (MONTH), 1967?

_________ times

---

51. Has (CHILD) been a patient in a nursing home, convalescent home, or any place like that, in the last 12 months--since (MONTH), 1967?

Yes . . . . (ASK A) 1

No . (SKIP TO INSTRUCTION AT BOTTOM OF THIS PAGE) 2

A. IF YES: Altogether, how many different times was (he/she) a patient in a nursing home, or any place like that, since (MONTH), 1967?

_________ times

IF CHILD WAS IN A HOSPITAL, NURSING HOME, OR SIMILAR PLACE IN LAST 12 MONTHS (YES TO Q'S. 50 OR 51), ASK Q. 52, ON NEXT PAGE.

IF NO TO BOTH Q'S. 50 AND 51, SKIP TO Q. 53, ON PAGE 20.

52. ASK A-F ABOUT EACH DIFFERENT STAY IN A HOSPITAL OR NURSING HOME (OR SIMILAR PLACE) IN THE LAST 12 MONTHS. START WITH THE MOST RECENT STAY. ASK A-F FOR EACH STAY BEFORE GOING ON TO THE STAY BEFORE THAT.

I'm going to ask a few questions about the time(s) (CHILD) was in the hospital (nursing home). (Let's start with the last time.)

	Most recent stay	Stay before that
A. When did (he/she) enter the (hospital/nursing home) (that time)? PROBE FOR MONTH AND YEAR.	Month Year	Month Year
B. How many nights was (he/she) in the (hospital/nursing home) (that time)?	______ Nights	______ Nights
C. What is the name and address of this (hospital/nursing home)? RECORD NAME, ADDRESS OR DESCRIPTION, AND CITY.	Name: ______ Add.: ______ City: ______	Name: ______ Add.: ______ City: ______
D. For what condition did (he/she) enter the (hospital/nursing home)--do you know the medical name? IF NAME NOT KNOWN, PROBE FOR SYMPTOMS, CAUSES, AND/OR PARTS OF BODY AFFECTED.		
E. Did (he/she) have any operations during this stay at the (hospital/nursing home)?	Yes (ASK [1]&[2]) . 1 No 2	Yes (ASK [1]&[2]) 1 No 2
IF YES TO E: [1] Can you tell me the name, or what kind of operation that was? IF NAME NOT KNOWN, PROBE FOR DESCRIPTION OF WHAT WAS DONE.		
[2] Any other operation (that time)? (IF YES: DESCRIBE.)	One operation only 1 Yes, other operation 2	One operation only 1 Yes, other operation . . . 2
F. Did you or (CHILD) see a doctor about (CONDITION) after (he/she) got out of the hospital?	Yes . . . . 3 No 4	Yes . . . . 3 No 4

Stay before that	Stay before that	Stay before that
________ Month Year	________ Month Year	________ Month Year
________ Nights	________ Nights	________ Nights
Name: ________ Add.: ________ City: ________	Name: ________ Add.: ________ City: ________	Name: ________ Add.: ________ City: ________
Yes . (ASK [1]&[2]) . . 1 No 2	Yes . (ASK [1]&[2]) . 1 No 2	Yes . (ASK [1]&[2]) . 1 No 2
One operation only . . 1 Yes, other operation 2	One operation only . 1 Yes, other operation 2	One operation only . 1 Yes, other operation 2
Yes . . . . 3 No 4	Yes . . . . 3 No 4	Yes . . . . 3 No 4

ASK EVERYONE:

53. When was the last time (CHILD) had a general physical check-up? (Just your best guess.)

(MONTH) (YEAR)

Never had one 0

C-54. A. Has (CHILD) ever had polio vaccine by mouth?

Yes 1

No 2

Don't know 3

B. Has (CHILD) ever had any polio injections or shots?

Yes 4

No 5

Don't know 6

C. Has (CHILD) ever had an injection or shot against measles?

Yes 7

No 8

Don't know 9

D. Has (CHILD) ever had any injections against diptheria, whooping cough, and tetanus--that is, DPT or baby shots?

Yes . . . (ASK [1]) . . . 1

No 2

Don't know 3

[1] IF YES TO D: How many DPT or baby shots has (he/she) had?

One 4

Two 5

Three 6

Four 7

Don't know 8

ASK EVERYONE:

55. About how long has it been since (CHILD), or you, or anyone in the household, saw or talked to a medical doctor about (CHILD'S) health--for any kind of condition, even for a few minutes?

_______ months OR _______ years

56. Altogether (including the visits we have already talked about), how many times in the last 12 months did (CHILD), or you, or anyone in the household, see or talk to a doctor, or go to any of these places, about (CHILD'S) health? First, to a hospital emergency room? . . . READ EACH CODE CATEGORY, AND RECORD NUMBER OF VISITS TO EACH. RECORD "0" IF NONE.

	# OF CONTACTS
A. Hospital emergency room	
B. Hospital out-patient clinic	
C. Clinic not connected with a hospital	
D. Private doctor, in his office	
E. Talk to a private doctor, over the telephone	
F. See a private doctor, in your home	
G. Did (CHILD) go anywhere else to see a doctor (not counting visits by a doctor while [he/she] was a patient in a hospital)? (SPECIFY)	
Total Contacts:	

That's a total of _______ visits and calls in the last 12 months--does that sound right? (IF NOT RIGHT, GO OVER CATEGORIES WITH RESPONDENT.

57. Altogether during the last 12 months, how many days did (CHILD) have to stay in bed, all or most of the day, because of illness or injury?

_______ days

Q'S. 58-59 OMITTED.

IF CHILD IS 2 YEARS OLD OR OVER, ASK Q. 60.

60. About how long has it been since (CHILD) was last treated or examined by a dentist?

_______ months or _______ years

Never X

IF WITHIN LAST 12 MONTHS, ASK A-D:

A. How many times has (CHILD) been to a dentist in the last 12 months?

_______ visits

B. When (he/she) last saw a dentist, was it for an emergency visit?

Yes 7

No 8

C. What has (he/she) had done by a dentist or assistant during the last 12 months? First, has (he/she) had (his/her) teeth checked, X-rayed or cleaned?

READ EACH ITEM, AND CODE "YES" OR "NO" FOR EACH.

	Yes	No
(1) Teeth checked, X-rayed, or cleaned	1	2
(2) Teeth fixed or filled	3	4
(4) Teeth or bridgework replaced	7	8
(5) Tooth or teeth pulled	1	2
(6) Any other work? (SPECIFY)	3	4

D. How long does it usually take (CHILD) to get to the dentist? (The way [he/she] usually goes?)

0-9 minutes 1

10-19 minutes 2

20-29 minutes 3

30-39 minutes 4

40-49 minutes 5

50-59 minutes 6

1 hour or more 7

Sees school dentist . . . 8

IF CHILD IS 5 YEARS OR OVER, ASK Q. 61.

61. What is the highest grade or year (CHILD) has completed in school?

No schooling	01
1st to 2nd grade	02
3rd to 4th grade	03
5th to 7th grade	04
8th grade	05
9th grade	06
High school, incomplete (grades 10 or 11)	07
High school, incomplete--plus vocational or business school . . .	08
High school, complete (12th grade) .	09
Vocational or business school, in addition to completing high school	10
College, incomplete	11
College, complete	12
Don't know	13

Q'S. 62-63 OMITTED.

END OF PINK BOOKLET FOR THIS CHILD;
FILL OUT ITEMS ON BACK OF BOOKLET AFTER
LEAVING HOUSEHOLD.

FILL OUT ITEMS BELOW IMMEDIATELY AFTER LEAVING HOUSEHOLD

A. Date of interview: ______________________

B. Interviewer's signature: ______________________

C. Respondent for this questionnaire was:

Respondent on main questionnaire . .	00
Someone else . . (ANSWER [1]) . . .	R

[1] IF SOMEONE ELSE: Who?

NAME: ______________________

PERSON NO.: . . . . [|]

CONFIDENTIAL
4055
9/68

Approved through-June 30, 1969

Form approved.
Budget Bureau No. 116-R0146

NATIONAL OPINION RESEARCH CENTER
University of Chicago

SEGMENT # ______________

DULS LINE # ____________

ASK Q. 87 AFTER ENTIRE INTERVIEW IS COMPLETED FOR ALL HOUSEHOLD MEMBERS.

87. If money was no problem, have you any suggestions on how health care can be improved?

A. Respondent for this questionnaire was:

Respondent on main questionnaire . 00

Someone else (ANSWER [1]) . . . . R

[1] IF SOMEONE ELSE: Who?

NAME: ______________________

PERSON NO.: . . . .

B. Interviewer's Signature:

____

NORC
4052
5-69

NON-INTERVIEW REPORT FORM

FILL OUT THIS FORM WHENEVER A MAIN QUESTIONNAIRE IS NOT CONDUCTED IN A HOUSEHOLD, OR ONE OR MORE SUPPLEMENTS (BLUE OR PINK) ARE NOT COMPLETED.

NAME (FULL NAME OF RESPONDENT IF AVAILABLE): ____________________

ADDRESS: ____________________ CITY AND STATE: ____________________

SEGMENT NUMBER: ____________________ DULS LINE NO.: ____________________

1. What part, or parts, of the interview have not been completed at this line number? (CODE AS MANY AS APPLY)

   Main Questionnaire 1

   Blue/Pink Booklet(s) (How many?) ______________ 2

2. Why were you unable to complete (ANSWER TO Q. 1)?

   Not home after ____ calls . . . 1

   Refusal . (ANSWER Q. 3) 2

   Break-off (ANSWER Q. 3) 3

   Temporarily unavailable (ANSWER Q. 4) 4

   No English (ANSWER Q. 5) 5

   Vacant DU 6

   No DU . . (EXPLAIN IN Q. 6) . . 7

   Other . . (EXPLAIN IN Q. 6) . . y

3. IF REFUSAL OR BREAK-OFF:

   A. Describe reason given for refusal or break-off.

   B. What do you believe was the reason for refusal or break-off?

3.--Continued

   C. Under what circumstances do you think the respondent could be persuaded to be interviewed?

4. IF TEMPORARILY UNAVAILABLE:

   A. Why is the respondent temporarily unavailable?

   B. When will the respondent be available?

5. IF NO ENGLISH: What language is spoken in the household?

6. Remarks:

(PLEASE FILL OUT BACK OF THIS FORM)

IF NOT-AT-HOME, REFUSAL, BREAK-OFF, OR UNAVAILABLE UNTIL AFTER FIELD PERIOD, TRY TO OBTAIN AS MUCH OF THE FOLLOWING INFORMATION ABOUT THE HOUSEHOLD AS POSSIBLE FROM WHEREVER POSSIBLE.

7. How many people live in this household?

Number: ____________________

---

8. What ages and sex are they?

AGE	MALES	FEMALES
Infants and children under 5 years old		
Children ages 5 to 13 years		
Adults 14 years old to 64		
Adults 65 and over		

---

9. Head of the household is --

White 1
Black 2
Oriental 3
Other (SPECIFY) 4

---

10. Longest time any member of the household has lived at this address -- (BEST GUESS)

Less than 6 months 1
6 months to less than 1 year . . . 2
1 year to less than 3 3
3 years to less than 5 4
5 years to less than 10 5
10 years or more 6

INTERVIEWER'S SIGNATURE: ______________________________

DATE OF REPORT: ______________________

APPENDIX E

RECORD-KEEPING FORMS

NORC
Log Form 1

MASTER CONTROL SHEET

Segment Number: ____________________

Interviewer ______________________

Date Originally Assigned __________

Orig. # of DU's in Sample ____
+ Tally of Extra DU's ____
- Tally of Vacant DU's ____
- Tally of No DU's ____

Total DU's
to be accounted for ____

Line No.	Case No.	Transf. to: (Int'r Name & Date)	Date		Temporary Status		Final Disposition				
			Va-cant	No DU	NIR type	NIR date	Compl. date	# Supplements		NIR type	NIR date
								Req.	Rec'd		

HOW TO PREPARE THE MASTER CONTROL SHEETS AND HOUSEHOLD FOLDERS

Case No. Column:

Starting with 0001, number in sequence giving each line the next number, using an automatic numbering machine.

From the listing sheets arranged in numerical sequence, record the segment number at the top of the master control sheet. Then record line number of all lines from the segment falling in the sample. The last numbered line should agree with the total number of household folders.

Number the household folders in sequence from 0001. From the listing sheets record on a separate household folder the segment number and line number for each line in the sample. Make sure that the case number on the household folder agrees with the case number on the master control sheet for each segment and line number.

NORC
Log Form 2

INTERVIEWER RECORD

Interviewer's Name: ______________________ Interviewer's Number: ______

Case No.	If transf: From whom?	Date Ass'd	Segment & Line #	Temporary Status		Transf. to: (Int. Name & Date)	Final Disposition			
							Compl. Date	# Suppl.		NIR Date

HOW TO LOG OUT ASSIGNMENT OF CASES

New Assignments:

1. Enter on the Interviewer's Record the case number and segment and line number of each Household Folder given to the interviewer.

2. Enter on the Master Control Sheet, for that segment, the name of the interviewer receiving the assignment.

Transfer of Cases:

This requires 3 entries:

1. Enter on the original interviewer's record the name of the person to whom the cases is being reassigned. This new name should be entered on the line of each case you are transferring.

2. Enter on the sheet of the new interviewer to whom the cases are being reassigned, the segment and line number of the cases being given her and the name of the person from whom it was transferred.

3. Enter on the Master Control Sheet, the date of transfer and the new interviewer on the line numbers she will have from that segment. Do not erase the original name at the top of the page.

HOW TO LOG IN COMPLETED CASES

On the Master Control Sheets

Find the Master Control Sheet for the segment. Find correct line number and case number and check to make sure they agree with what is written on the Household Folder for the case and on the Main Questionnaire and all supplements. Enter the date (preferably in red) in the "Final Disposition" column under "Compl. Date."

Now turn to enumeration table on page 2 of the Main Questionnaire and count the number of supplements required; record that number in the "# Suppl. Req." column next to the date you just entered. Then count the number of supplements actually received and enter this number in pencil (if it is not the same as the total number required) in the "# Suppl. Rec'd" column. When additional supplements are actually received, put corrected total in this column.

On the Interviewer Record Sheets

Find the sheet for the particular interviewer. Check the segment and line number as well as case number columns to make sure these numbers are correct on all documents. Then record date (preferably in red) in the "Final Disposition" column under "Compl. Date." Also check the number of supplements as per instruction for the Master Control Sheets and enter correct information in the "# Supplements Req. and Rec'd" columns.

HOW TO LOG IN NIR's (Non-Interview Reports)

VACANCIES or NO DU's: Both of these are logged in the same way.

1. On the Interviewer Record, write in the Final Disposition NIR column either the word "VACANT" or "NO DU" on the proper line number and the date.

2. On the Master Control Sheet, ENTER date in the proper column on the line number, and put a hash mark (/) at the top of the page where the count for that segment is kept.

These NIR's are then placed in a file folder. One folder is made up to hold all vacancies, another folder is made up to hold all NO DU's. It's a good idea to file within each folder numerically according to segment and line number within segment.

REFUSALS: Before logging in refusals, give them to your supervisor to review. In most cases these will be called "Temp. Refusals" at first, because we will want to try our best to convert them into a good interview, if possible. The supervisor will write in pencil on the outside of the folder containing the "Refusal" NIR, the word "Temp. Ref.," and return it to you to be logged in. You then--

1. On the Interviewer Record, FOR THE line number, write in the date and "Ref." in the Temporary Status column.

2. On the Master Control Sheet, do the same.

The temporary refusals are then put into a folder which the supervisor will review and perhaps reassign to another person.

Now, when a case has been determined as a final refusal and nothing more will be done on it, the supervisor will write on that household folder in colored pencil the words, Final Ref., and it is ready to be logged in as a final loss:

1. On the Interviewer Record, in the last column (the one called Final Disposition) you enter in colored pencil "REF" and the date.

2. On the Master Control Sheet, write in colored pencil "REF" and the date in the Final Disposition column under NIR type and NIR date.

OTHER NIR's: Follow the same pattern as for entering refusals, just use the proper name for the type of loss it is, such as Too Ill, Moved Away, Not Home, etc.

Do not give case numbers to any NIR's. Make up separate folders to hold each category of NIR's. For instance, all Vacancies are filed together, and the same is true for NO DU's, Temporary Refusals, Final Refusals, Moved Away, Too Ill, Not Home, etc.

NORC
Log Form 3

PROGRESS REPORT

For Week Ending: ____________
(date)

Initial Sample Size ________
+ Extra DUs ________
- Vacancies ________
- No DUs ________
Net Sample ________

Number of Completed Cases ________

Completion Rate ________%

RECAPITULATION

IN OFFICE — Number of Completed Cases ________

Final NIRs

- Refusal ________
- Break-off ________
- Not-at-home ________
- Too Ill ________
- Unavailable for duration of field period ________
- Moved ________
- Land. Probl. ________
- Other ________

Total Final NIRs + ________

Temporary NIRs

- Refusal ________
- Break-off ________
- Not-at-home ________
- Too Ill ________
- Temp. Unavailable ________
- Moved ________
- Land. Probl. ________
- Other ________

Total Temporary NIRs + ________

IN FIELD

Reassigned NIRs ________
Original Cases ________

Total in Field + ________
Net Sample = ________

Number of Active Interviewers ________

NORC
Log Form 4

DAILY TAKE RECORD FOR ____________
Date

Interviewer	# Main Quex Compl.	# Suppl.		# NIR's Rec'd.	Remarks
		Req.	Rec'd.		
1.					
2.					
3.					
4.					
5.					
6.					
7.					
8.					
9.					
10.					
11.					
12.					
13.					
14.					
15.					
16.					
17.					
18.					
19.					
20.					
21.					
22.					
23.					
24.					
25.					

Daily Total Completed Main Quex __________

Accumulated Total Completed Main Quex __________

HOW TO LOG IN EXTRA DWELLING UNITS[1]

1. Go to Interviewer Record and add an "A" to the line number affected for that segment. Then, at the end of her listing, add the segment and line number of each of the other added line numbers, such as B, C, D or whatever.

2. Go to Master Control Sheet. Enter an "A" to the line number affected. Then, add the additional units with the accompanying B, C, D, or E as indicated.

3. Initial the Extra Dwelling Unit Report[2] and file in folder containing these sheets.

---

[1]An extra dwelling unit can turn up as an address already listed if the interviewer goes to the address and discovers that there is actually more than one dwelling unit at the listed address. See Administrative Specifications in Appendix D for interviewer instructions about this phenomenon.)

[2]See Appendix C for a copy of this report.

APPENDIX F

QUALITY-CONTROL MATERIALS

norc

national opinion research center
UNIVERSITY OF CHICAGO
6030 South Ellis Avenue,
Chicago, Illinois 60637
684-5600 Area Code 312

MEMORANDUM

TO New York Office

FROM William C. Richardson

SUBJECT Guidelines for Field Editing
Survey 4055

DATE 10/16/68

A. General

Check the entire questionnaire of each family member and the family section on the respondent's quex for completeness, correct skip patterns, and mechanical consistency (that is--correct number of booklets, correct Segment and DULS Line Numbers, etc.)

B. Internal Consistency

The following areas are particularly subject to problem of consistency:

1) If there is an episode, and if Q. 30 is "yes," the number of visits in Q. 37 becomes the minimum number in Q. 56. Q. 55 must be 12 months or less.

2) Q. 43 must be at least 2 days.
Q. 44 must be no more than Q. 43.
Q. 44 becomes the minimum for Q. 57.

3) If there are hospital days, these become a part of the minimum for Q. 57.

C. Missing Information

A phone call or call-back is indicated in cases where responses to any of the following questions are missing:

4B, D	24	48 & 48A	61
6	26A, B, C	50	68
17-18	37	51	71
19-22	43	56	83
	44	57	

Other questions that have been missed should be picked up if there is a call-back, or if it is economical for the interviewer to stop by, and if they can be re-asked out of context.

WCR:tt

5/69

NATIONAL OPINION RESEARCH CENTER
University of Chicago

Case No.

FOLLOW-UP INTERVIEW FORM

Interviewer Number

Respondent's Name: ____________________

Hello, Mrs. ____________, I am ____________ from the Neighborhood Health Center. One of our interviewers visited you recently to interview you about your health and the health of the other members of your household. I would like to thank you for your cooperation in this study. I am (here/calling) now to get just a little additional information. The questions I have to ask will take only five minutes.

First, I would like to check your address. READ ADDRESS; IF DIFFERENT, RECORD CORRECT ADDRESS AND CONTINUE THIS INTERVIEW.

Street Address: ____________________

Telephone Number ____________

Own Phone 1
Neighbor's Phone 2

Time Interview Completed: ____________ AM
PM

Date Interview Completed: ____________

Sex of Interviewer: Male 1

Female 2

RECORD OF CALLS				
Date	T	P	Validator	Remarks
1.				
2.				
3.				
4.				
5.				
6.				

1. About how long was the interviewer at your home--was it just a few minutes, about half an hour, an hour, or more than that?

Just a few minutes	1
About half an hour	2
An hour	3
More than an hour	4

---

2. Did (he/she) complete the interview on one visit or did (he/she) have to come again?

One visit	1
Come again	2

---

3. In general would you say you enjoyed the interview a great deal, somewhat, not very much, or not at all?

Very much	(ASK A)	1
Somewhat	(ASK A)	2
Not very much	(ASK B)	3
Not at all	(ASK B)	4

IF VERY MUCH OR SOMEWHAT:

A. What were some of the things you enjoyed?

IF NOT VERY MUCH OR NOT AT ALL:

B. What were some of the things you didn't like?

4. Do you think the health survey is a very good thing for the community, somewhat good, or not too good?

Very good 1
Somewhat good 2
Not too good 3

---

5. How many people are there in this household--including yourself?

One	1	Seven	7
Two	2	Eight	8
Three	3	Nine	9
Four	4	Ten	0
Five	5	Eleven	X
Six	6	Twelve or more	Y

---

6. For which members of your household did (he/she) fill out a booklet?

---

7. You said that most of the time you go to a ________________ when you want to see a doctor for yourself.

If you could choose and you didn't have to think about cost, where would you prefer to go--to a private doctor, hospital clinic, or somewhere else?

Private doctor 1
Hospital clinic 2
Somewhere else 3

---

8. You said there were ________ rooms in your (apartment/house), not counting bathrooms--and that ________ of these are used for sleeping.

Do you feel you have enough rooms for yourself (and your family) or would you like more?

Enough 1
Would like more 2

9. Have you ever been interviewed on a survey before this one?

Yes . . . . (ASK A & B) 1
No 2

IF YES:

A. How many times? ________ times

B. What (was it/were they) about?

---

10. Can you describe the interviewer to me (just briefly)?

---

11. Is there anything else you would like to say about the interview or the person who interviewed you?

APPENDIX G

INTERVIEWER REPORT FORM

CONFIDENTIAL
4052

5-69

NATIONAL OPINION RESEARCH CENTER
University of Chicago

INTERVIEWER REPORT FORM

NORC learns a great deal from what our interviewers tell us. Please be assured that your responses will be kept confidential. Please enter your interviewer number in the three digit boxes above but you need not sign this report form.

---

1. In general, would you say you enjoyed working on this survey a great deal, quite a bit, only a little, or not at all?

Great deal 1
Quite a bit 2
Only a little 3
Not at all 4

---

2. In general, how do you think most people in the area felt about being interviewed?

They enjoyed it 1
They didn't mind 2
They disliked it 3

---

3. In general, do you think most, some, or hardly any of the people you interviewed told you accurately about the medical problems and care they have had?

Most of them 1
Some of them 2
Hardly any 3

---

4. Which questions do you think were most difficult for the respondents to answer? (PLEASE GIVE NUMBER FOR EACH QUESTION MENTIONED.)

A. Why do you think these questions were difficult to answer? (WRITE QUESTION NUMBER NEXT TO COMMENT.)

5. Which questions do you think were <u>easiest</u> for the respondent to answer? (PLEASE GIVE NUMBER FOR EACH QUESTION MENTIONED.)

   A. Why do you think these questions were easy for the respondent to answer? (WRITE QUESTION NUMBER NEXT TO COMMENT.)

---

6. Here is a list of different kinds of jobs. Which one do you think is <u>most</u> like the job of an interviewer, and which do you think is <u>least</u> like the job of an interviewer? CIRCLE ONLY ONE IN EACH COLUMN.

	Most like the job of an interviewer	Least like the job of an interviewer
Artist who paints pictures	1	1
Teacher	2	2
Playground group leader	3	3
Waitress	4	4
Nurse	5	5
Newspaper reporter	6	6
Singer in a night club	7	7
Health aide	8	8
Clothes presser in a laundry	9	9
Saleslady in a store	0	0
Social worker	X	X

---

7. Do you think that your respondents answered most, some, or hardly any of the interview questions accurately?

   Most 1
   Some . . (ANSWER A & B) . 2
   Hardly any (ANSWER A & B) . 3

   <u>IF SOME OR HARDLY ANY</u>:

   A. Which questions didn't they answer accurately?

   B. Why do you think they didn't?

8. We know from past experience that interviewers find some parts of the job difficult and other parts easy, and that there are differences among interviewers about which are difficult and which are easy.

Now that you have finished your work on the health survey, please tell us which parts of your job were very difficult for you, which were fairly difficult, which were fairly easy, and which were very easy for you.

	Very difficult	Fairly difficult	Fairly easy	Very easy
Knocking on doors	1	2	3	4
Locating the dwelling units	1	2	3	4
Maintaining rapport--that is, having a comfortable and friendly relationship with the respondent	1	2	3	4
Editing your work	1	2	3	4
Getting through the interview--that is, keeping the respondent on the track and being business-like about your job	1	2	3	4
Reporting to your supervisor	1	2	3	4

9. Do you see interviewing as good training for another job?

Yes . . . (ANSWER A-C) . . 1
No X

IF YES:

A. What kind of job?

B. How did interviewing prepare you for it?

C. What do you think your chances are of getting a job you described in A within the next six months to a year?

Excellent 1
Good 2
Fair 3
Poor 4

10. How good an interviewer do you think you are?

One of the very best . . . 1
Above average 2
Average 3
Below average 4

11. Please indicate whether you agree or disagree with each of the following statements.

	Agree	Disagree
A. Good luck is just as important as hard work for success.	1	2
B. Very often when I try to get ahead, something or someone stops me.	4	5
C. Most people can be trusted.	7	8
D. People like me don't have a very good chance to be really successful in life.	1	2

We always learn from interviewers' suggestions and would appreciate it very much if you would give the following questions careful thought.

12. In what ways could your interviewer training sessions have been made better so as to have been more help to you on your actual assignment? (GIVE DETAILS.)

A. In what ways could you have been helped more by the Health Survey supervisors during the field work?

13. How could the interviewer's manual have been improved to be of more help to you in the field?

14. What kinds of things did you find most successful in getting respondents to do the interview?

---

15. Are there any other comments, criticisms, or suggestions you would like to make about anything on this study which was not touched upon by the questions in this form? (IF YES, PLEASE EXPLAIN.)

---

16. Were there any particularly interesting, unusual, sad, or humorous experiences you had on this study that you would like to tell us about here?

Thank you very much for your help.

APPENDIX H

JOB-PLACEMENT MATERIALS

JOBS: A Major Objective of the OEO Neighborhood Health Center Baseline Research Program in Atlanta, Georgia, August 26, 1968

By Fansayde N. Calloway

One of the most challenging and enjoyable aspects of my assignment to train community residents in the professional art of interviewing was OEO's sub-objective of providing new career ladders and incentives for them. Since all but one of the staff of twenty-two had been unemployed prior to this job, my plan was to seek positions or further training which would represent a step ahead or certainly be in line with the level at which they were now able to perform. The results are summarized below with accompanying description of how this was achieved.

Firm Commitments for Placement

In conference with the Co-Director of the Comprehensive Health Center, and its Personnel Director, the following six positions were obtained at the Center:

Research Assistant
Appointments Secretary
Receptionist
Switchboard Operator
Clerk-Typist Trainee
Clerk-Typist Trainee

A seventh placement was secured as housemother at a local day nursery. (Recently I received a phone call from its director telling me how pleased she was with the employee.)

The eighth firm commitment was a position as cashier-trainee with the Atlanta Housing Authority

Future Employment Possibilities

... The Comprehensive Health Center has promised to consider personnel for positions as Community Health Assistants, X-ray Assistant, and related jobs, once the date for the opening of the permanent site is determined.

... The Atlanta Housing Authority will notify interviewers when their fall program is operative. (Discussed later.)

... The ACEP New Careers Program will contact interviewers when their fall program begins. (Discussed later.)

Educational Pursuits

Two interviewers were interested in entering a two-year training course at a local hospital as X-ray technicians. In a telephone conversation with the Fulton-DeKalb Hospital Authority, I was told that there was a "crying" need for paramedical personnel, and particularly X-ray technicians--that money was no object. Various funding plans and scholarships were available. I sent two persons to apply who were high school graduates. They were told that college entrance exams should be taken, but that the results would not affect their acceptance. The cost of the exam was $15.00 and would be given two days later. Both failed the exam and were told that because of this they could not be accepted. They were the only two applicants taking the exam from the School of X-ray Technology that day. The others were applicants for the School of Nursing and regular entrants to Georgia State College. One would wonder if the School of X-ray Technology had only two applicants for the fall semester.

High School Equivalency Tests

Six of the staff without a high school diploma desired to take the equivalency test. One took it recently, and a tutoring class is in the process of being set up to assist the other five. I have been assured by the Comprehensive Health Center that when its Education Director returns from vacation, he will make the necessary plans to provide space for this purpose.

Other Training Plans

I have advised the staff to take the clerical aptitude test battery and those who have the potential should enroll in typing and related business course classes in order to qualify for the various civil service exams for city, county, and state jobs. The Director of the local Manpower Office has agreed to set up the testing for them.

About the Staff

The staff was recruited from the area in southwest Atlanta which is served by the Comprehensive Health Center. Early in the training program, I was impressed by the native intelligence of the group and their desire not only to learn the new skill of interviewing, but also to improve themselves generally for future employment. It became increasingly clear that the mainstream of our economy was overlooking valuable human resources. After learning of their frustration in taking training courses which resulted in no job placements and of their awakened ambition to study and take the high school equivalency test in those instances where a diploma was lacking, after observing their sustained and successful efforts to do a compentent job of data-gathering, I felt there was no alternative to lending an all-out effort to aid them in finding upwardly-mobile jobs. It seemed unconscionable to allow them slump back into the same directionless state from which they had emerged. They had taken pride in the knowledge that they were selected from among 110 applicants, and had worked hard at improving their performance. As a tangible result, their interviewing completion rate was 92 per cent, with only a 3 per cent refusal rate. It was with great reluctance that they accepted the 5 per cent "other" losses, which included not-at-home, etc.

How the Plan Evolved

Approximately three weeks before the field work ended, I began a concentrated effort to locate jobs. Being a stranger to the city, I was convinced that an imaginative approach was necessary to appeal to those who could be of help. I decided that I needed the assistance of a community person who knew the power structure and persons in top positions in the city, county, and state; one who had the respect of those to whom the appeal would be made. The person who best fit this description was the Honorable Grace T. Hamilton, a Negro member of the State Legislature, a native Georgian, a former national YWCA staff member, and former head of the Atlanta Urban League. It should be noted that Mrs. Hamilton is not elected from the district in which the Center is located. However, she is a personal friend who has been interested and kept abreast of the research program from the day I arrived.

When approached, she graciously accepted the task and immediately began correspondence and phone calls to strategic agencies and persons as shown in the attached documents. Simultaneously, I also developed a list from other friends to pursue in the same manner. In several instances there was duplication of agencies, but this served to emphasize the importance and urgency of the mission, rather than to detract from it.

Some Conferences and Phone Calls

Since correspondence does not appear for conferences and phone calls, I would like to share the following with you:

I. EOA-NAB Conference

Those present:

Chief of Manpower, EOA, and liason with the National Alliance of Business Men
Coordinator of Manpower, EOA
Associate Director of Manpower, ACEP
Chief of EOA Centers

The chief of EOA Centers, a personal friend, arranged the conference. The EOA representatives were sympathetic to the aims, and it was arranged that the director of the local Manpower office would come to the Health Center and take individual applications and learn of their job interests.

Special mention must be made of the local Manpower office director, who not only came to meet the interviewer group, but personally escorted them in groups of five to the downtown Professional and Clerical Office and remained with them until each had been interviewed and some evaluation made. This took two days of his time. The State Commissioner of Labor cooperated in this program. He is presently working on job placements and has promised his cooperation on a continuing basis after my return to Chicago.

The ACEP representative indicated that he had immediate openings in a department store in a town about 15-20 miles from Atlanta. But upon further inquiry I learned that the pay was below the minimum hourly wage, so I told him this was not desirable. To travel four to five hours each day and receive below minimum wages would only perpetuate their sub-standard status, and was certainly not feasible for women with family responsibilities.

In considering the development of new job possibilities, I asked about such sources which serve the community as the local loan offices, discount houses, etc. These businesses have a multitude of white-collar jobs. The NAB representative indicated that an owner of a loan office chain was on the committee, and suggested that the Associate Director of Manpower, ACEP, contact him.

Some Personal Observations of the Manpower Service

The job placement interviewers are rather limited in their effectiveness. For instance, some persons were sent on job interviews where the specifications from the employers were clear that certain prior experience was necessary. The placement personnel seem to lack the initiative or ability to attempt to sell the employer on related qualifications which might be applicable. As a result, the applicants spent their limited funds in useless travel with resulting discouragement.

Job development personnel are not as skilled as is necessary to "sell" employers on new opportunities. Their practice of accepting jobs below the minimum wage is self-defeating. It perpetuates the theory that those for whom they seek placement are not worth a living wage.

Despite good intentions, people such as the local Manpower office director are hampered by the "system." Since he is new to the community, there is the possibility that he can build up the image of the office. In general, the community-at-large holds the Manpower office in rather low regard. And since the EOA Center and Manpower are so intimately connected, its reputation tends to affect EOA as well.

The fact that the local director took the group to the downtown office shows that jobs relegated to the outlying communities probably are those least desirable. However, the new Commissioner of Labor seems interested in upgrading the system, and was most cooperative in this venture.

II. Atlanta Housing Authority Conference

Those present:

Associate Executive Director
Chief Personnel Director
Chief of Relocation Branch

Mrs. Hamilton had written to the Associate Executive Director, and in the meantime, I had lunch with the Chief Personnel Director, a personal friend, and apprised him of the job project. He called later that same day with an appointment set for two days hence.

The Associate Executive Director was impressed with the program and generously gave time for a detailed discussion. He told me of the long-range plans of the Authority and of the several programs to be launched in the fall which could use the skills of the interviewers. The Chief Personnel Director supplied me with application forms for the entire group to be sent to his personal attention.

After some persuasion, it was agreed that an immediate opening for a cashier-trainee was possible. I was to refer four persons from which to select. Two white and two Negro women were sent. Since this occurred just before I left Atlanta, I do not know which one was selected. The other applications were sent in for consideration in the fall for such jobs as relocation aides.

III. Fulton County Civil Service Commission Phone Call

A representative called at the instigation of Mrs. Hamilton with the information that jobs were open for clerk-stenographers, clerk-typists, and clerk-typist trainees. I told her that since these women were not just out of school, whatever good typing skills they may have had years ago had now been lost. However, there were two women who might qualifty as clerk-typist trainees since their speed need only average 30 words per minute. Those qualified were given this information. Since this also came at the time of my departure, I do not know the results.

IV. Conference re New Careers Training Program

The Interim Coordinator was optimistic that some of the interviewers could be offered training opportunities once the New Careers budget had been approved. She was given the roster for notification in the fall when the recruitment begins.

<u>In Conclusion</u>

Because of my deep conviction in the overall objective of the OEO program to aid persons in breaking the poverty cycle and because of my recognition of the frustration that can set in when one is gainfully employed, does a creditable job, and is then faced with the same old seemingly insurmountable obstacles, the efforts put forth in Atlanta seemed the least that should be done. My real regret is that the demands of the ongoing research left insufficient time to begin job scouting earlier and to be present in Atlanta until job placements or training plans were further along the way.

There was a distinct advantage in my being a "stranger." One of the obvious selling points expressed by several of those with whom I met was that I did not <u>have</u> to become involved to this extent. On the other hand, I think it was crucial that I be paired with someone from the community who shared this same concern and had entree to the proper sources. This was not a chore but a privilege for both of us.

Attached are copies of correspondence and lists of most of the contacts made in pursuit of the goal for jobs.

FIELD CORRESPONDENCE

norc

national opinion research center
UNIVERSITY OF CHICAGO

July 24, 1968

To Whom It May Concern:

I wish to request your assistance in the placement in upward-mobile jobs of about twenty-one women who are currently employed as research interviewers for the Comprehensive Health Center in Southwest Atlanta.

To give you a little background---under a grant from OEO, the Neighborhood Health Centers in several cities are developing ambulatory health service programs for a target population. To assist in their program planning in Atlanta, the National Opinion Research Center, University of Chicago, was contracted to conduct a household survey among approximately 1,000 families in the target area bounded by Georgia Avenue, Lakewood, the Expressway and Hill Street, to do the following:

1. On a sampling basis, to update census information on the area's population.

2. To delineate from this population the families and characteristics of families eligible for services at the Center.

3. To determine general health services utilization patterns, and some indicators of impairments which now exist.

Since the overall objective of the OEO program support is to aid persons in breaking the poverty cycle, NORC did not use its regular trained staff, but instead, area residents were trained in professional interviewing techniques in an effort to provide new career ladders and incentives for them.

Training lasted about six weeks and included such essentials as developing the professional art of verbatim recording, probing for clarity and additional information, establishing rapport with all kinds of people, convincing reluctant people to be interviewed, how to read with clarity and recognize when questions have been answered to the point, how to deal with clerical aspects of the work, such as listing of dwelling units in the area, filling out questionnaire forms accurately, computing elapsed time, computing income where required.

The questionnaires used on the study to obtain health data on all family members consisted of a 36 page main questionnaire, plus a 16 page booklet for each family member, and an 8 page supplement relating to the public's attitudes toward doctors, psychiatric-oriented services and dental practices.

Although this type of field work is normally done by persons with a minimum of some college education, I am pleased to find that the quality of work done by these indigenous persons measures up most favorably, and in some instances has excelled that of regular staff interviewers.

I have been impressed also with their native intelligence, personableness, personal appearance, responsiveness to suggestion, honesty, motivation, and perception. Although the refinement in spelling and sentence construction which comes with formal education is lacking, in most instances there is no problem in understanding their recordings.

Because of their good performance, I am convinced that they would be a valuable asset to any employer, and would become as competent as regularly hired employees. Therefore, I am most desirous to find suitable placements in private industry or public agencies (other than temporary Government projects). They are motivated to obtain permanent jobs in the mainstream of our economy. May I also add that there has been no problem with absenteeism without cause.

Their previous work experiences have ranged from domestics to a supply teacher. I feel they can perform responsibly in general office jobs, such as file clerks, bookkeeping clerks, cashiers, receptionists, switchboard operators, nursery school attendants, jobs requiring dealing with the public either over counters or in home visits, and interviewing.

I will greatly appreciate any help you can give in making these qualifications known to those who can use the talents of these women, 19 of whom are Negro and 2 who are white. They will be available in mid-August. Of course, if an opportunity arose earlier, I would be willing to release some of them in the interest of a permanent job.

Attached is a summary which gives an overall picture of the group.

My sincere thanks for your interest.

Sincerely yours,

(Mrs.) Fansayde N. Calloway
Assistant National Field Director

FNC/sls

CHARACTERISTICS OF INTERVIEWING STAFF

A. Ages range from 21 years to 49 years.

Age Group	Number of Interviewers
21-29	8
30-39	7
40-49	6
	21

Average age is 35 years.

B. Grade Completed in School

Year	Number of Interviewers
9th Grade	1
10th "	3
11th "	4
High School Diploma	12
2 years College	1
	21

Five of above are studying to take the high school equivalency test.

C. Marital Status

Married	12
Widowed	3
Separated	5
Single	1
	21

D. Number of Dependent Children

Number of Children	Number of Interviewers
None	3
1 Child	4
2 Children	5
3 "	1
4 "	2
5 "	5
7 "	1
	21

AGENCIES CONTACTED IN ATLANTA, GEORGIA

Mayor
City of Atlanta
City Hall

Vice Mayor
City of Atlanta
40 Pryor Street, S.W.

Director
City of Atlanta Personnel Board
City Hall Annex
260 Central Avenue, S.W.

Commissioner
Georgia Department of Labor

Chairman
National Alliance of Businessmen
Trust Company of Georgia
36 Edgewood Avenue, N.E.

Executive Administrator
Economic Opportunity, Atlanta
101 Marietta Street

Chief of Manpower and NAB Liaison
EOA
101 Marietta Street

Coordinator of Manpower
EOA
101 Marietta Street

Associate Director of Manpower
Atlanta Concentrated Employment Program
101 Marietta Street

Chief of EOA Centers
101 Marietta Street

Chairman
Fulton Company
Commissioners of Roads and Revenues
165 Central Avenue

Associate Executive Director
Atlanta Housing Authority
824 Hurt Building

Personnel Director
Atlanta Housing Authority
824 Hurt Building

Chief of Relocation Branch
Atlanta Housing Authority
824 Hurt Building

Interim Coordinator
New Careers Program - EOA
101 Marietta Street

.power Director
.rice Community EOA Center
1127 Capitol Avenue, S.W.

Director
Carrie Steele Pitts Nursery
667 Fairburn Road, N.W.

President
The Coca Cola Company
P.O. Drawer 1734

Fulton County Civil Service Board
Room 310 - Adm. Bldg.
165 Central Avenue, S.W.

Deputy Administrator
Fulton County Family and Children's Services
165 Central Avenue, S.W.

Registrar
Fulton-DeKalb Hospital Authority
80 Butler Street

Director
State Department of Family and Children Services
State Office Building